Wilfred H. Baker, B.S.C.E., M.S.C.E., Syracuse University, is Professor of Civil Engineering at West Virginia University. He has been a photogrammetrist with the U. S. Forest Service and an engineer in charge of aerial surveys in New York State for the U. S. Agricultural Conservation Service. Professor Baker also assisted in the acreage-control program of the Agricultural Adjustment Administration.

ELEMENTS

OF

PHOTOGRAMMETRY

WILFRED H. BAKER

PROFESSOR OF CIVIL ENGINEERING
WEST VIRGINIA UNIVERSITY

THE RONALD PRESS COMPANY · NEW YORK

Library of Congress Catalog Card Number: 60–14858

PRINTED IN THE UNITED STATES OF AMERICA

PREFACE

The elements of photogrammetry are presented in this book, with particular emphasis on the physical and mathematical principles involved. Photogrammetry is followed logically through the successive stages of planning an aerial survey, the flight, the production of photographs, ground control, and the use of the photographs, beginning with the simpler devices and progressing to the more complex stereoplotting equipment.

The book has developed from many years of teaching an elementary course in the subject to civil engineering classes. Fundamental principles have been emphasized, especially with respect to the vertical photograph and the theory and use of the stereoscope, an instrument upon which all photogrammetrists are so dependent in one way or another. Although intensive training in the use of complex plotting instruments is more appropriate to advanced courses, this and other topics are introduced to stimulate student interest in further reading and research.

Varied numerical problems are provided, which are suitable either as home assignments or as supplements to the laboratory work. Ample laboratory work is suggested for either two or three semester hours, depending upon the availability of photographs and equipment.

The author wishes to express his grateful appreciation to all those individuals, companies, and government agencies that have so kindly supplied photographs and other material. The statements of interest and good wishes were most encouraging. Finally, he expresses thanks to his wife, who not only typed the manuscript but suggested changes for its improvement.

WILFRED H. BAKER

Morgantown, West Virginia
October, 1960

CONTENTS

ELEMENTS

OF

PHOTOGRAMMETRY

1

INTRODUCTION

1–1. Definition of Photogrammetry. Derived as it is from three Greek roots meaning "light–writing–measurement," the word *photogrammetry* refers to the art and science of making measurements on photographs. It is also usually extended to include the use of these measurements in bringing forth a resulting product and sometimes the production of the photographs themselves. It may readily be appreciated that photogrammetry can be used in many fields, such as geology, forestry, agriculture, and even medicine and archaeology, to mention but a few, but the principal applications that will be considered throughout this text are in the field of surveying and mapping.

1–2. Development. The development of photogrammetry has been intimately connected with that of the camera and photographic materials and processes. Since photography from the air has advantages over that taken on the ground for mapping purposes, the growth of aerial photogrammetry was quite rapid following the inception and manufacture of suitable aircraft. In its own right, the history of photogrammetry consists largely of the development of instruments possessing various ranges of complexity for the transformation of photographs into maps or survey information. Also may be included the development of graphical and analytical methods of accomplishing all or part of these same ends.

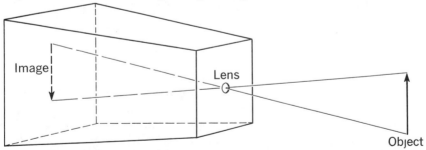

Fig. 1–1. Sketch of a camera obscura.

1–3. The Camera. The modern camera had its origin in the camera obscura (Fig. 1–1), credit for the invention of which is sometimes given to Giovanni della Porta in 1553, although it seems certain that the principle was known and used much earlier. Subsequent developments included the use of lenses, diaphragms, and portable boxes, so that early in the eighteenth century the camera obscura had become a regular article of commerce. These devices merely caught the image of the landscape or subject without retaining it; another hundred years elapsed before images were successfully fixed on plates. In 1822 the first permanent photograph was made by J. N. Niopce. Plates of metal or glass were used at first, but as the result of a search for something lighter and more flexible, the roll film was developed in 1884 by George Eastman and W. H. Walker.

1–4. Aircraft. The earliest work in photogrammetry was done with pictures made at ground stations. Aerial photographs were first taken from kites and captive balloons beginning about 1860, but the greatest advances resulted from the development of the dirigible and the airplane, especially during World War I. While the camera's position could not be directed with a high degree of accuracy in these types of aircraft, they were yet far superior to the balloon, which was at the complete mercy of air currents. It was about 1913 that the first photograph for mapping purposes was taken from an airplane.

1–5. Early Beginnings. The science of photogrammetry dates from about 1850 when Colonel Aimé Laussedat, often called the father of photogrammetry, first utilized measurements from photographs for the compilation of map data for the French army. Development of the new science was slow because of the limitation of photography and the usual resistance to new methods, but the ideas and principles had been founded. In 1888 Captain Edouard Deville of Canada developed a practical method of using stereoscopic photographs in a single instrument for drawing a map.

1–6. European Workers. From Canada, the interest and progressive efforts were transferred to Europe, where many became active in the development of automatic plotting instruments. Workers there included Dr. A. Meydenbauer in Germany, M. Chevallier of France, and Captain Theodor Scheimpflug of Austria, the last of whom in 1904 developed an eight-lens camera which was attached to the basket of a balloon. Thus a forerunner of the most modern of composite cameras (Art. 1–9) was constructed almost as soon as the single-lens mapping camera itself.

1–7. Instruments. The use of photographs for mapping purposes was greatly enhanced by the invention and development of various instruments, especially the stereoscopic ones, which make possible the simultaneous viewing of two photographs of the same area taken from different stations. An important feature of many of these is the floating mark, the principle of which was discovered in 1892 by F. Stolze and adapted to measuring instruments by Dr. C. Pulfrich. All the modern stereoscopic plotting or measuring instruments described in later chapters utilize this principle. The discovery of the stereoscopic effect itself and the construction of the first stereoscope is credited to a noted British physicist, Sir Charles Wheatstone, about 1835.

1–8. Early Use in the United States. Mapping agencies of the United States government did not take readily to the innovation and were somewhat behind Canada in this respect. The method of radial plotting (Chapter 6) was developed by C. B. Adams of the United States Army in 1893, and terrestrial photogrammetry (Chapter 12) was used in 1894 by the Coast and Geodetic Survey for topographic mapping on the Alaska-Canada boundary survey. Here, as in other countries, aerial photogrammetry was little known or used until the development of the airplane in World War I.

1–9. Coast and Geodetic Survey. In 1920 the Coast and Geodetic Survey revised the topography of the charts along the New Jersey coast from aerial photographs taken by the Army Air Corps, and photogrammetric surveys have been used continuously by the Survey since 1928. A nine-lens camera

Fig. 1–2. Nine-lens aerial camera. Although all the lenses are parallel, eight of them take oblique views by means of mirrors, which can be seen at the lower part of the camera. (Courtesy of Coast and Geodetic Survey.)

(Figs. 1–2, 1–3) was constructed in 1936 under the direction of O. S. Reading, with the cooperation of the Bureau of Standards and the Fairchild Camera Corporation. A Division of Photogrammetry was organized in the Survey in 1945.

1–10. Geological Survey. The United States Geological Survey used a panoramic terrestrial camera for topographic surveys in Alaska as early as

Fig. 1–3. Photograph taken with the nine-lens camera. (Courtesy of Coast and Geodetic Survey.)

1904. In 1920 the planimetry of the Schoolcraft, Michigan, quadrangle was mapped with single-lens aerial photographs, the contours being added by topographic methods in the field (Art. 6–27). A section of Photographic Mapping was established in 1921, and in 1927 the Survey imported a Hugershoff Aerocartograph from Germany, the first automatic stereoscopic plotting instrument utilizing aerial photographs to be owned by an agency of this government.

1–11. Recent Developments. A tremendous need for maps arose with various new or expanded programs of the government about 1933, and photogrammetry had developed sufficiently to assume a major part of the huge task which was thus thrust upon the map-makers of the nation. An expanded land acquisition program for National Forests, the development of the Tennessee Valley, and a vast program of farm crop control by the Agricultural Adjustment Administration all required maps or area surveys. The latter agency alone was eventually to be responsible for aerial photography covering some 2,500,000 square miles. These demands were instrumental in the organization of many air-surveying companies, the development of cameras and related equipment, and the training of an increased number of photogrammetrists and technicians in this field (Fig. 1–4).

FIG. 1–4. Expert cartographers adding place names and reviewing previous compilations from aerial photographs. (Courtesy of Bausch & Lomb Optical Co.)

1–12. Writers. The development of methods and instruments has been accompanied by a literature on these subjects by workers in photogrammetry and related fields. A list of the more prominent early writers would include Aimé Laussedat of France, Reinhard Hugershoff and Otto von Gruber of Germany, Martin Hotine of England, Edouard Deville of Canada, and Earl Church of the United States.

1–13. Education. Photogrammetry, as it developed in theory and applications to the field of surveying and mapping, began to be introduced into college curricula and, like surveying itself, has usually been placed in civil engineering departments. It may have been inserted as a part of the regular courses in surveying or made a distinct course, either as a requirement or as an elective. In a. few instances, photogrammetry has been offered under a separate department or as an option in the civil engineering curriculum.

The first major course in photogrammetry in the United States was established at Syracuse University in 1929 under the direction of Professor Earl Church. This was made possible by grants from the Daniel Guggenheim Fund for Aeronautics to be used for the purchase of instruments and equipment. Syracuse was selected because of its pioneer work in this field, a course in terrestrial photographic surveying having been required in the civil engineering curriculum since the founding of the engineering college in 1902. The new program established by these grants included eight courses, ranging from map-making and aerial navigation to the economics of aerial mapping. Soon afterward a graduate program was established, which attracted many students both from the United States and from foreign countries.

1–14. American Society of Civil Engineers. One of the technical divisions of the American Society of Civil Engineers, founded in 1852, is devoted to the fields of surveying and mapping. The development of photogrammetry has been increasingly noted in the work of this division, and for the past several years a large proportion of its papers has been directly or indirectly concerned with photogrammetry and its applications to surveying and mapping problems. These papers are published in the *Proceedings* of the Society and many of them are also included in the annual *Transactions*.

1–15. International Society for Photogrammetry. The International Society for Photogrammetry was founded in Austria on July 4, 1910, and serves to facilitate the exchange of ideas and information among the photogrammetrists of the world. It organizes the International Congresses and Exhibitions for Photogrammetry which, since 1926, have been held regularly at four-year intervals except during World War II. The 7th Congress was held at Washington, D. C., in 1952, the 8th at Stockholm in 1956, and the 9th was set for London in 1960. Publication of the quarterly journal, *Photogrammetria*, which was started in 1939 and interrupted shortly thereafter because of the international situation, was resumed in 1949. Technical commissions of the society include Photography and Aerial Navigation; Plotting Instruments and Techniques; Aerial Triangulation and Geometric Computations; Mapping and Commercial Applications; Miscellaneous Applications; Education, Terminology, and Bibliography; and Photo-Interpretation.

1–16. American Society of Photogrammetry. The American Society of Photogrammetry was founded in 1934 with 217 charter members. Its first president was Colonel C. H. Birdseye, and some of the other prominent men in photogrammetry who have been honored with this office include O. S. Reading, Virgil Kauffman, Marshall S. Wright, and George D. Whitmore. Membership is open to those who are directly or indirectly working in the field of photogrammetry and to students engaged in undergraduate or graduate work in any university or school recognized by the Society. The student members are entitled to all the privileges of the Society except the right to vote.

The annual meeting, usually held in Washington, D. C., brings together those who are interested in photogrammetry, for the presentation and discussion of papers and an interchange of ideas and problems. The Society publishes *Photogrammetric Engineering*, a quarterly journal containing news, papers, and articles of benefit to those engaged in or interested in this field. It has also published the *Manual of Photogrammetry*, first in 1944 and a revision in 1952, a comprehensive volume covering the major divisions of the subject written by active workers in the field.

Aside from these publications, other major achievements of the Society include the development of standard specifications for aerial photography (largely through the efforts of Colonel H. H. Blee, the Society's second president), precision camera specifications, and specifications for map accuracy.

1–17. American Congress on Surveying and Mapping. The first meeting of the American Congress on Surveying and Mapping was held in Washington, D. C., in 1941 and was sponsored by the following five groups: the Committee on Surveying and Geodesy of the (now) American Society for Engineering Education, the Surveying and Mapping Division of the American Society of Civil Engineers, the American Society of Photogrammetry, the Federal Board of Surveys and Maps, and the National Geographic Society. Its first president was Robert H. Randall.

The first listing of the technical divisions of this organization included one for Photogrammetric Mapping, with Virgil Kauffman as chairman, and a second entitled Surveying and Photogrammetric Instruments, with H. M. Dibert as chairman. However, in 1956 neither of these divisions existed as such, the field of photogrammetry evidently having been absorbed in the other divisions, which were Cartography, Control Surveys, Education, Instruments, Property Surveys, and Topography.

2

AERIAL PHOTOGRAPHY

2–1. Aerial Surveys. Aerial photography for surveying and mapping purposes has been increasingly used in this and other countries by various governmental agencies. A large part of the United States is covered by aerial photography, most of it having been done by private companies under contract with the U. S. Geological Survey, the U. S. Coast and Geodetic Survey, and agencies of the U. S. Department of Agriculture. Some of this photography has been utilized for accurate mapping, while some has been used for rough mapping and the calculation of farm areas. Other uses* for aerial surveying may be listed: highway surveys, pipe line location, and route surveys in general; geological surveying and exploration; and the preparation of cadastral and administrative maps. Aerial photography is especially suitable for reconnaissance surveys for routes, where some measure of secrecy is desirable to avoid an inordinate raising of land prices.

It is to be appreciated that the economy of using aerial photography depends upon the size of the area to be covered. An aerial survey would probably not be justified for a single farm of 100 acres, while it undoubtedly would be justified for an entire state or even a county. It would be impossible to set a definite size of area marking the division between a profitable and an unprofitable aerial survey, for there are too many factors which would vary in different instances. It would seem that the burden of the photography must be assumed by large companies and government organizations, but once the photographs are available, the private surveyor or engineer may find many ways of using them for making location studies and reconnaissance, and even an accurate survey or map of a relatively small area.

2–2. Cameras. The cameras used in aerial photography (Figs. 2–1, 2–2, 2–3) are manufactured with a high degree of precision. Negatives on glass plates are preferred for accuracy because of their low differential expansion and small distortion from a plane surface at the time of exposure. However, films are not so expensive or bulky, each roll containing from 100 to 200 exposures in a relatively small space.

The aerial camera is of fixed focus, since it is always used at an altitude sufficiently high to be considered infinite. As indicated in Fig. 2–4, it consists of a light-tight chamber at one end of which is a lens and shutter assembly

* Further descriptions and examples of applications are given in Chapter 13.

FIG. 2–1. Type K-17 mapping and reconnaissance cameras, 9-in. by 9-in. photographs, 12-in. and 6-in. focal lengths. (Photo from files of Gordon Enterprises.)

FIG. 2–2. Type CA-6a camera, 4-in. by 5-in. photographs, 15-in. focal length, used for hand-held oblique photography. (Photo from files of Gordon Enterprises.)

(Fig. 2–5) to control the admission of light. At the opposite end is the focal plane, which, for the infinite object distance, is placed at exactly the focal distance from the lens. To complete the camera, there is a magazine to hold both the exposed and unexposed plates or films.

There are three principal types of shutters: between-the-lens, focal plane, and louver. The first is most commonly used because of its durability and freedom of obstruction in the opening. Lying between the component parts of the lens itself, it consists of a series of curved, thin blades hinged on the periphery of a circular ring and is activated by a suitable mechanism for opening and closing. Speeds may range from 1/100th to 1/500th of a second.

In the focal plane shutter (Fig. 2–6) an opaque curtain lies immediately below the camera's focal plane. Upon release, the curtain moves across this plane, carrying a narrow slit from one side to the other, thus providing an extremely small time exposure for any portion but a relatively long time for the entire photograph. While images are sharp as a result of the fast exposure, they may be relatively displaced from one side of the picture to the other.

The louver shutter consists of a number of parallel slatlike parts mounted in a rectangular frame, each being free to rotate about its own longitudinal

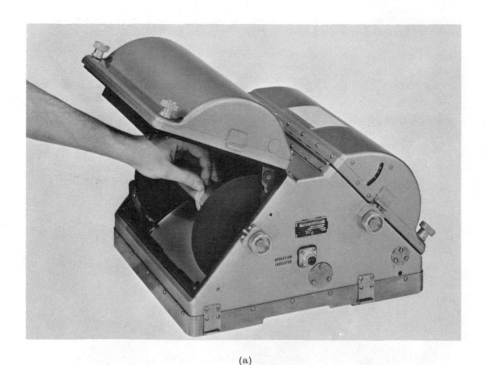

(a)

Fig. 2–3. Type T-11 mapping camera, disassembled. (a) Magazine holding 390 feet assembly in camera body. (Courtesy of

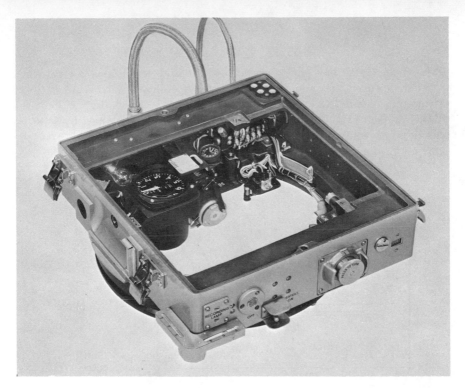

(b)

(c)

of film; (b) data-recording equipment in camera body; (c) lens cone and shutter
Fairchild Camera & Instrument Corporation.)

axis. When lying flat, they form an opaque and continuous cover; when rotated, however, they allow light to pass the openings formed between them. While this type has the good features of the focal plane shutter without the disadvantage of the long total exposure time, it is handicapped by a rather cumbersome construction and an inertia in the moving parts. Too, the louvers form a partial obstruction to the passage of light through the lens.

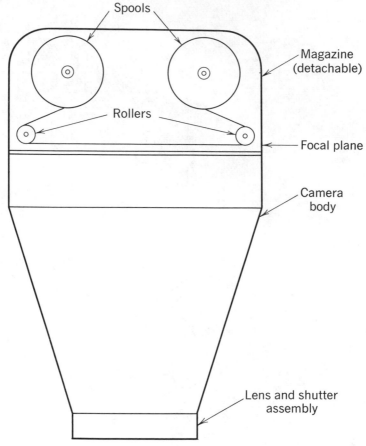

FIG. 2–4. Schematic drawing of aerial camera.

2–3. Airplane. The airplane used in aerial photography for mapping purposes is usually relatively light, although for stability a heavier one might be more desirable. A suitably located hole must be provided in the floor for the camera mount (Figs. 2–7, 2–8), due regard being taken for the convenience of the photographer. A four-passenger airplane would seem the smallest desirable, affording room for the pilot, the photographer, the camera, and, if desired, an extra person to aid with the navigation and to give instructions to the photographer.

FIG. 2–5. Aerial camera lens and shutter assemblies. (Courtesy of Fairchild Camera & Instrument Corporation.)

FIG. 2–6. Focal plane shutter. (Courtesy of Fairchild Camera & Instrument Corporation.)

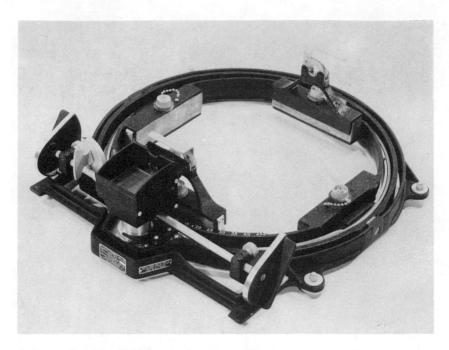

Fɪɢ. 2–7. Manually operated camera mount. (Photo from files of Gordon Enterprises.)

Fɪɢ. 2–8. Special Steinheil gyro-optical stabilizing aerial camera mount. (Photo from files of Gordon Enterprises.)

Regular flight instruments are of course essential for the proper maneuvering of the airplane, maintaining the required altitude and speed, and keeping on the prescribed course. A vertical viewfinder (Fig. 2–9) indicates the ground area over which the airplane is flying, together with its direction

FIG. 2–9. Vertical viewfinder. (Photo from files of Gordon Enterprises.)

and speed relative to the ground. In addition, a gyrocompass or sun compass may be used to keep the flight lines straight and in the required direction.

Lens Theory

2–4. General. A consideration of the basic physical relationships in the camera lens is helpful in the development of certain photogrammetric principles. The function of the lens is to gather light reflected from the ground and transmit it to the photographic surface. Its quality will, therefore, have a marked effect upon the accuracy of the resultant photograph.

An elementary lens consists of a single piece of glass, the surfaces of which are spherical, as shown in Fig. 2–10. The line $X—X$ connecting the two centers of curvature is called the *optical axis*. In the lens shown, both of the

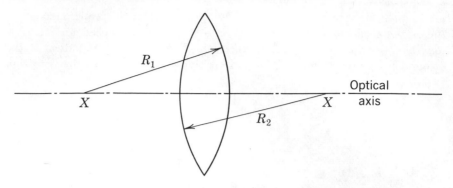

FIG. 2–10. An elementary lens.

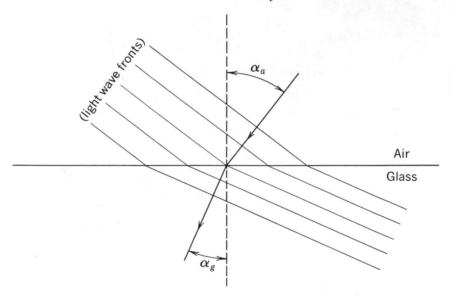

FIG. 2–11. Refraction of light waves.

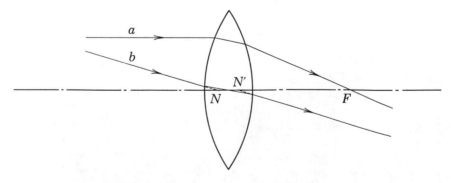

FIG. 2–12. Principal focus and nodal points.

surfaces are convex, but one could be a plane (radius of curvature infinite) or one or both could be concave. In order to achieve certain characteristics, combinations of two or more different lens elements are used in a single-lens system, and the effect of each element would need to be investigated to determine the net effect of the entire system. However, the purpose of this discussion will be served if the system is considered replaced by a single equivalent lens element, as shown in Fig. 2–10.

2–5. Index of Refraction. The velocity of light varies with the density of the medium through which it passes, being slower for glass than for air. The ratio of its velocity in free space (commonly considered the same as in air) to that in another medium is called the index of refraction of that medium. If successive wave fronts from a light source are indicated, as in Fig. 2–11, it will be observed that the light waves are bent at the boundary line of the two mediums as a result of the difference in velocity. When one medium is free space (or air), the *index of refraction* can be shown to be $\sin \alpha_a / \sin \alpha_g$. It is convenient to think of light as traveling in straight lines, which are called *rays*, which would be perpendicular to the wave fronts of Fig. 2–11. The rays are then bent toward the normal to the surface in the medium of greater density. A ray which strikes the boundary at right angles will suffer a change in velocity but no deviation in path.

2–6. Principal Focus. There are an infinite number of light rays emanating from any object, only a small portion of which actually strike the lens surface. The behavior of some of these will now be considered in their relation to certain points of the lens. The ray at a in Fig. 2–12, parallel to the optical axis on one side of the lens, is refracted by the lens and crosses the axis at F. All such rays in a perfect lens will likewise pass through F, and this point is called the *focal point* or *principal focus*.

2–7. Nodal Points. All rays, except those that strike a surface perpendicular to it, are bent both upon entering the lens and upon leaving it. The ray at b, however, is one of a number that are bent in such a way that its direction upon leaving is parallel to that at entering. If both the entering ray and the exiting ray are extended, they will intersect the axis at N and N', which are called the *nodal points*. Thus any ray passing through a nodal point is undeviated in direction. This is important in photogrammetric theory because it is the basis for the assumption that the geometrical relations in the camera are similar to those from lens to ground, as shown in Fig. 2–13. The points N and N' are the front and rear nodal points, respectively, but since the distance between them is very small compared with the flying height of the airplane, it is commonly assumed that they coincide at N'.

2–8. Focal Length. The camera lens brings all the rays which strike it from a point on the ground to a common intersection at the image on the photograph. The distance from the rear nodal point to the principal focus is called the focal length,* and the relationship among the distance from lens to object (O), distance from lens to image (I), and the focal length (f) is: $1/O + 1/I = 1/f$.

Since, in aerial photogrammetry, the camera is at a height that can be considered infinite, it follows that the image should be placed at a distance from the lens equal to the focal length, and the altitude of the photograph triangle is equal to f.

The precise determination of the focal length is a problem for the optical laboratory, but an approximate determination may be suggested by Fig. 2–13. If the camera can be set in a position so that the object signals A and B

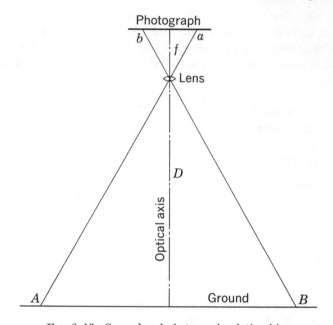

FIG. 2–13. Ground and photograph relationship.

are on a line perpendicular to the lens axis, then, after measuring the distances AB and D on the ground and ab on the photograph, by similar triangles, $f = (ab/AB)D$.

2–9. Aberration and Distortion. In the foregoing discussion, it has been assumed that the lens system is perfect, and that the rays from a point object all intersect exactly in the corresponding image point. In an actual lens, there are several reasons why they may fail to behave in this ideal way. One of these is shown in Fig. 2–14. In a perfect lens all the parallel rays from a distant object would converge to a single point focus at F, but in an actual lens, the rays nearer the edge intersect nearer the lens, while those near the

* *Focal length* may be defined in several ways, but this is the most satisfactory for photogrammetric purposes.

center intersect farther from the lens. The consequent blurring of the image due to this cause is called *spherical aberration*. A similar blurring of images off the axis is called *coma*.

When white light passes through the lens, its various color components may be separated because of their slightly different wavelengths, as indicated in Fig. 2–15, so that the various colors come to a focus at slightly different

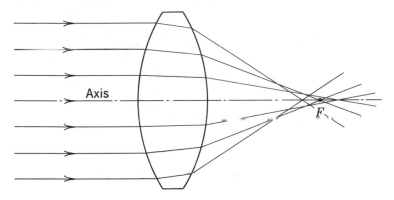

Fᴵɢ. 2 14. Spherical aberration.

points along the axis. This is called *longitudinal chromatic aberration*. For oblique rays there will be fringes of colors for images near the outer portions of the field. This is called *lateral chromatic aberration*.

The failure of the nodal point rays to pass through undeviated over the

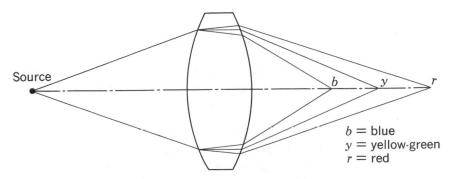

b = blue
y = yellow-green
r = red

Fɪɢ. 2–15. Chromatic aberration.

whole field results in image displacements radially from the center, as shown in Fig. 2–16. This is called *lens distortion*.

Aberrations and distortions may be greatly reduced by the proper combination of different curvatures and glass with different indexes of refraction. A few of these are shown in Fig. 2–17.

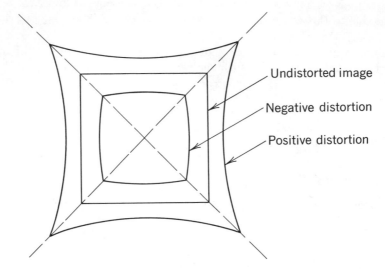

FIG. 2–16. Effects of lens distortion on images.

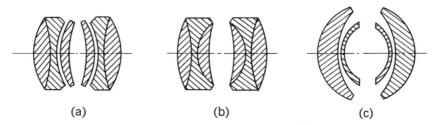

(a)   (b)   (c)

FIG. 2–17. Some photographic lenses; (a) and (b) are normal-angle lenses, (c) is a wide-angle lens.

Planning the Flight

2–10. Photograph Requirements. For mapping purposes, the photographs must be taken in a systematic order, both to assure that the area is completely covered and to satisfy certain requirements of the various photogrammetric processes. Photographs are usually taken in straight, parallel strips a distance apart so that the areas covered by any two adjacent flights overlap by from 25 to 30 per cent. Furthermore, the area covered by any two successive photographs within a strip should overlap by about 60 per cent (Fig. 2–18). This seemingly excessive overlap is necessary because for most mapping processes every point on the ground must appear in at least two and some in three consecutive photographs. With 60 per cent overlap in adjacent photographs, there will be 20 per cent overlap between alternate exposures. Finally, the photographs must be approximately to some specified scale. It may thus be appreciated that careful planning is necessary before the flight itself is made.

2–11. Scale. A simplified diagram of the relation between a vertical*
photograph and the ground is shown in Fig. 2–19. L is the camera lens at a
height H above the datum; f is the distance from lens to photograph which,
for aerial photography, is the focal length. Vv is the vertical line through L,
which is assumed to coincide with the camera axis. P is a ground point

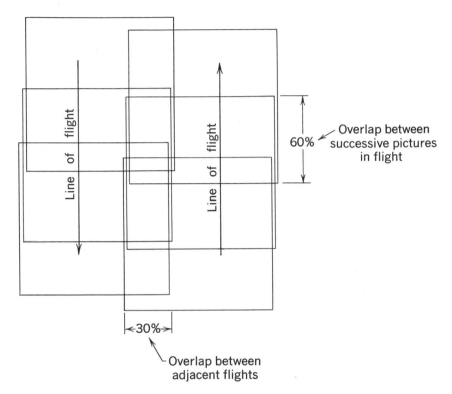

Fig. 2–18. Diagram showing conventional overlap of aerial photographs and flights.

whose image on the photograph is at p, it being assumed that the light passes
through the lens without deviation.

The triangles vLp and VLP are similar, so

$$\frac{LV}{Lv} = \frac{H}{f} = \frac{VP}{vp} \tag{2–1}$$

The latter term represents the ratio between corresponding ground and
photograph distances and thus may be called the *scale* of the photograph.
However, photograph scale is an indefinite quantity, as will now be shown.
Suppose P is raised vertically to P', the horizontal distance $V'P'$ remaining
equal to VP. The image on the photograph will move outward to p' so that

* For definition of vertical photograph, see Art. 5–1.

the ratio $V'P'/vp'$, or scale, is not the same as VP/vp, its former value. Thus the scale of a photograph should be designated at some specific ground elevation.

2–12. Flying Height. H in Fig. 2–19 represents the flying height of the airplane above the datum surface. From Eq. 2–1, $H = f \cdot VP/vp$, or the

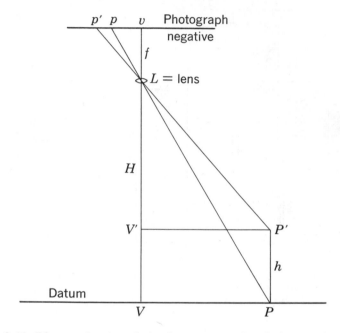

Fig. 2–19. Diagram showing relation between ground and photograph points.

focal length times the scale at datum. If the scale is specified for some elevation h above datum, then

$$H = f \cdot \text{scale} + h \qquad (2\text{–}2)$$

Thus, to determine the flying height above sea level for photographs at a specified scale, the ground elevation is added to the calculated flying height above the ground surface.

Example 2–1. What altitude above sea level must be flown to produce a photograph scale of 1 in. = 2000 ft. if the camera focal length is $8\frac{1}{4}$ in. and the average ground elevation is 1500 ft.?

Flying height above ground = 8.25 × 2000 = 16,500 ft.
Average ground elevation   =   1,500
Flying height above sea level   = 18,000 ft.

2–13. Coverage. With its "average" scale and dimensions known, the extent of ground covered by each photograph is readily computed.

EXAMPLE 2–2. Some 7-in. × 9-in. photographs are to be taken at an average scale of 1 in. = 2000 ft. What is the ground coverage in each direction?

$$7 \times 2000 = 14{,}000 \text{ ft. in the short dimension}$$
$$9 \times 2000 = 18{,}000 \text{ ft. in the long dimension}$$

The net coverage of each photograph is then calculated on the basis of specified overlaps.

EXAMPLE 2–3. For the values of the preceding example, what are the net longitudinal and lateral coverages of a photograph, if the forward dimension is 7 in.? Use overlaps of 60 and 30 per cent, respectively.

$$\text{Net forward coverage} = (1.00 - 0.60) \times 14{,}000 = 5600 \text{ ft.}$$
$$\text{Net lateral coverage} = (1.00 - 0.30) \times 18{,}000 = 12{,}600 \text{ ft.}$$

These are the distances between successive exposure stations and adjacent flight lines, respectively.

2–14. Exposure Interval. If the ground speed of the airplane and the net forward coverage of the photograph are known, the time between successive photograph exposures can be determined.

$$\text{Time} = \text{Distance/Speed}$$

EXAMPLE 2–4. For the preceding examples, the ground speed of the airplane is 100 mph. What is the interval between exposures in seconds?

$$\text{Time} = \frac{5600}{100 \times 5280} \times 3600 = 38.2 \text{ sec.}$$

2–15. Flight Map. The distance between adjacent flight strips is determined as in the example above. The center lines of the proposed flights are then marked off on the best available map of the area. This map should show all the major features, especially the complete road system and the principal streams and other bodies of water. A series of such features can usually be chosen along each plotted line to assist the pilot in keeping the airplane on the desired course.

Specifications commonly require photography beyond the limits of the area for a distance· equal to the amount of sidelap between flights. This will fix the line of the first flight with respect to one side of the area. If the other flights are then set off at the calculated interval, it may happen that the last flight extends an undue amount beyond the opposite boundary. Although no saving is necessarily effected, it may be considered more desirable to shorten the distance between adjacent flight lines sufficiently so that this overhang will be closer to the required value. The sidelap throughout the entire project will thus be increased, but this is normally not objectionable.

2–16. Number of Photographs. The length of a flight line as scaled from the map, divided by the net coverage of each photograph in the forward direction, gives the number of photographs necessary for the strip. To ensure complete coverage, it is customary to require two photograph centers beyond the boundary at each end, or a total of four extra pictures in each flight. The summation for all flights gives the total number of photographs for the area, and from this is determined the number of film or plate magazines that will be needed.

2–17. Time Required. The total length of the flight lines divided by the anticipated average ground speed gives an estimation of the time necessary for the actual photography. To this must be added allowances for turning at the end of each flight, for changing magazines, and for traveling from and to the airport. The total time may be important in determining whether more than one mission will be needed because of limitation of fuel supply or available photographic time in the day.

EXAMPLE 2–5. An area 20 mi. by 40 mi. is to be photographed, using the camera and specifications of the preceding examples, flight lines being parallel to the long dimension. Determine (1) the number of flight lines, (2) the total number of photographs, and (3) the time required for the mission, excluding travel from and to the airport. Assume 120 exposures to a roll of film, 5 min. to turn at the end of each flight, and 10 min. to change magazines.

1. Width of area $= 20 \times 5280 = 105{,}600$ ft.

   Add for overhang at side

   of area: $\quad 0.30 \times 18{,}000 = \quad \underline{5{,}400^*}$

   $\qquad\qquad\qquad$ Total $= \overline{111{,}000}$ ft.

   Number of flight lines $= \dfrac{111{,}000}{12{,}600} = 8.8$; use 9 (the next higher integer)

2. Length of each flight[†] $= 40 \times 5280 = 211{,}200$ ft.

   Number of photographs in flight $= \dfrac{211{,}200}{5{,}600} = 37.7$; use 38

   $\qquad\qquad$ Adding four extra at ends $\qquad\qquad = \underline{\ 4}$

   $\qquad\qquad\qquad$ Total, each flight $\qquad\qquad = \overline{42}$

   Total number of photographs $= 9 \times 42 = 378$

3. Number of rolls $= \dfrac{378}{120} = 3.15$; use 4, with 3 changes in flight

   Length of each flight, approximately $= 41 \times \dfrac{5600}{5280} = 43.5$ mi.

   Total flight for photography $= 43.5 \times 9 = 391.5$ mi.

* It will be noted that the width is increased by the overhang on only one side, the other being accounted for by the *gross* width of the first flight.

† In practice, the area may be of irregular shape, making it necessary to figure each flight line separately.

$$\text{Time of actual photography} = \frac{391.5}{100} = 3.915 \text{ hr.} = 235 \text{ min.}$$

Time for turns $= 8 \times 5$ $= 40$ min.

Time for changing magazines* $= 3 \times 10$ $= 30$ min.

               Total time $= 305$ min. or

                                          5 hr. 5 min.†

The Flight Mission

2–18. Preparation. After the flight has been planned, the actual flying and photography have yet to be performed. The airplane must be made ready, with the camera in place and with sufficient film magazines either to complete the job or to allow full utilization of the available flying time. The crew, consisting of at least a pilot, a cameraman, and perhaps an additional person as an aide, must be ready to take immediate advantage of favorable weather and flying conditions.

2–19. Time of Flight. Specifications often restrict flight missions to a certain season in order to obtain some desired condition with regard to the ground surface. For example, it is commonly specified that no snow shall be on the ground and that no leaves shall be on deciduous trees. In the northern parts of the United States this would necessarily restrict the flight to early spring or late fall, although shadows will be longer, especially in the autumn, than if the flight were made nearer the beginning of summer. In any event, the flight should normally be made as close to midday as possible in order to take advantage of the best lighting and the shortest shadows.

2–20. Weather. The most desirable conditions would be a cloudless sky and the complete absence of wind. Clouds may hide the ground surface or cast shadows upon the ground even though they themselves do not appear in the photograph. An occasional cloud may be avoided by skillful flying, but where there are too many, the flight breaks and jumps that become necessary would undoubtedly be unsatisfactory. There is also an objectionable lack of continuity in the photographs of a flight strip where parts are flown at different times. However, since perfect flying days are all too few, it may in the long run be more economical to utilize less than perfect cloud conditions at the expense of some "cloud hopping."

2–21. Flying Requirements. In flying the airplane, the pilot must accomplish the following: (1) Attain and maintain the calculated flying height, (2) locate the desired flight path and follow it for the prescribed distance, (3) maintain the ground speed for which the exposure interval of the successive

---

* Sometimes part of this may be included in the turns.

† If this time is greater than that available for photography in the day or from the fuel capacity, a recalculation should be made accordingly. When figuring on fuel capacity, travel from and to the airport must also be included, together with a reserve for safety.

photographs has been predetermined, and (4) keep the airplane on an even keel at the time of each exposure.

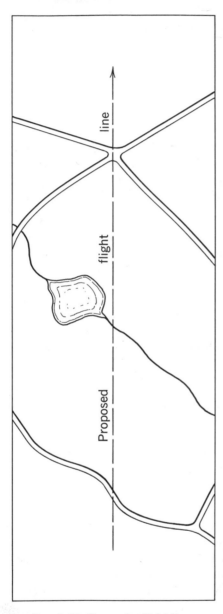

FIG. 2–20. Range for flight line

2–22. Flying Height. The flying height is measured by an altimeter, which can be set to read altitudes with reference to sea level. Since this is a barometric-type instrument, depending upon the pressure of the atmosphere, allowances must be made for the changes of pressure which occur with varying atmospheric conditions. The proper settings are obtained as a regular part of aerial navigation from the statistical information provided by the U. S. Weather Bureau. If the area to be photographed is far enough from the airport, the necessary altitude may be attained on the way. Otherwise the airplane must be circled until the required flight altitude is reached.

2–23. Ranges. The desired flight lines will have been marked on the flight plan map. Along or close to each line, ground points are selected which can be seen from the airplane and afford a *range* to be followed. Thus, in Fig. 2–20, the distinct bend in the crossroad and the edge of the pond fall on the flight line and would serve to establish the range. As the road falls behind, the crossing beyond the pond may be discerned and thus the range continued, a new point in the distance being selected each time the near point passes from sight beneath the airplane. Furthermore, the compass bearing may be read after the range has been established from landmarks; then this same course is maintained until additional points are descried on the line ahead. It is to be noted that this compass reading is not usually the bearing of the line desired on the ground, but rather the direction in which the airplane is *headed*. That the two are not often the same is an effect of the wind, as shown in Fig. 2–21. Thus, for parallel flights made in opposite directions, the compass readings will usually differ by something other than 180 degrees, according to the direction and intensity of the wind. If these are known, the required heading to produce a desired ground bearing at a given speed can be determined. This is a common problem in aerial navigation.

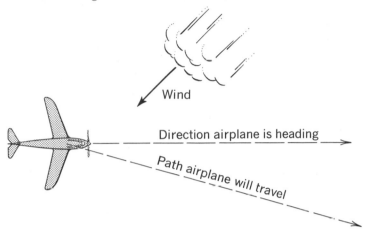

Wind

Direction airplane is heading

Path airplane will travel

Fig. 2–21. Effect of wind on path of airplane.

2–24. Speed. The airplane's speed shown by the indicator is relative to the air rather than to the ground, the two speeds being different because of the wind. If the photographs are to be taken at a precalculated time interval based upon a certain ground speed, a determination of the required air speed must be made, taking into account the direction and force of the wind. Again, this can be done as a part of the navigational problem mentioned above. The air speed would normally be different for a flight in the opposite direction. If the camera is to be operated manually at intervals to be determined by observing the passage of the terrain through a viewfinder, the determination of ground speed is not important.

2–25. Photography. In commencing a flight strip, the pilot should maneuver the airplane onto the range well outside the area so that the approach will be at a uniform speed and on level keel. The latter is very important, especially at the instant of exposure. As the airplane approaches the area, the camera is started in sufficient time to provide the specified coverage beyond the boundaries. Exposures are then continued at the appropriate intervals to provide the specified longitudinal overlap until the other end of the strip is reached. Again the pilot maintains the course and a level keel well beyond the limits of the area to provide the specified coverage, care being exercised not to begin the turn until the camera is stopped. A circle is then made to the next flight line, and the procedure is repeated.

2–26. Changing Film. When one roll of film has been consumed, it is necessary to change magazines, the one containing the exposed film being lifted from the top of the camera and another holding an unexposed roll slipped into its place. Normally this operation takes considerably more time than the interval between exposures. A change of magazines at the end of a flight strip results in less loss of time, since it can usually be done at the same time that the pilot is maneuvering into position on the new flight. However, since it is not often that the film will run out exactly at the end of a flight line, this procedure may waste a few feet of film. Should the waste be excessive, it may be better to change magazines in the middle of a flight. If so, the airplane must be circled while the change is being made and then brought back onto the line so that the first photograph of the new roll will give the required overlap with the last photograph of the previous roll. To be on the safe side, commonly the two portions are made to overlap by three or four photographs rather than to attempt exact matching. A similar procedure, in so far as flying is concerned, would be necessary where a part of a flight has been omitted because of cloud conditions.

2–27. Reflights. After the photographs have been processed in the dark-room, they are inspected for compliance with specifications, especially as to overlap, coverage, clouds, and tilt. If any photographs are unsatisfactory, one or more reflights must be made to replace those which were rejected. With a few exceptions, the reflight is similar to the original. If the fault is one of flying, such as insufficient lateral overlap, the reason for this must be determined and corrected. Perhaps the layout map was not sufficiently accurate to provide parallel and equidistant flight paths. Each reflight is started ahead of the break and carried beyond it to provide a satisfactory juncture between the original and reflight photography. It is well if the reflight can be taken at about the same time of day as the original flight so that the shadows will be in about the same position, but of course this is not always practicable.

PROBLEMS

2–1. What is the scale of a photograph taken with an 8.25-in. focal length camera at a height of 15,000 ft. above the ground?

2–2. What flying height is necessary to give a scale of 1 in. = 2000 ft. with a 12-in. focal length camera?

2–3. A camera of what focal length would be necessary to give a scale of 1 in. = 1500 ft. at a flying height of 10,000 ft.?

2–4. How many square miles are covered by a 7 × 9-in. photograph at a scale of 1 in. = 1650 ft.?

2–5. What is the distance between photographs and the distance between flights for 7 × 9 in. photography at a scale of 1 in. = 1800 ft. if the overlaps are 60 and 25 per cent, respectively, and the short dimension is parallel to the line of flight?

2–6. What is the time interval between exposures for Prob. 2–5 if the ground speed of the airplane is 90 mph?

2–7. A rectangular area 30 mi. by 50 mi. is to be photographed at an "average" scale of 1 in. = 2000 ft. with an 8.25-in. focal length camera, flight lines to be parallel to the long dimension of the area. The photographs are 9 × 9 in., the forward overlap is 60 per cent, and the sidelap is 30 per cent. The average ground speed is 120 mph. Each roll provides 150 exposures. Calculate (a) the total number of photographs, and (b) the total time for the flight, not including travel from and to the airport. Allow 5 min. for turning at the end of each flight and 10 min. for changing magazines.

2–8. Using the same photographic information and specifications as for Prob. 2–7, calculate the number of photographs and total time for the area shown in Fig. 2–22.

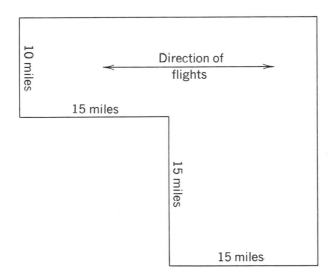

Fig. 2–22. See Problem 2–8.

LABORATORY PROBLEM

Lab. Prob. 2–1. Given specifications for aerial photography as in Problem 2–7 above, modified and supplemented as desired by the instructor, plan a flight for an assigned area as defined on some available map. A county highway map or a portion of one or more Geological Survey quadrangle sheets would be suitable. Determine the total number of photographs and film rolls needed, as well as the total time and time interval between exposures. Plot the proposed flight lines on the map and select several landmarks along each one to aid in keeping on course. Estimate the cost of the project after obtaining current prices for flying and photography, assuming that two contact prints of each negative are to be furnished.

Note: Comparisons may be obtained by assigning different scales and different directions for the flight lines.

3

PHOTOGRAPHS, INDEXES, AND MOSAICS

3–1. The Photographic Laboratory. No attempt will be made to cover the subject of the photographic laboratory completely; only the major steps and processes required to transform the aerial negative into a product that can be used by the photogrammetrist will be discussed here. Thorough information on the chemistry of the photographic processes and operations of a photographic laboratory is readily available from a number of sources.

3–2. The Darkroom. For processing the photographs, it is essential to have a darkroom (Figs. 3–1, 3–2, 3–3) equipped with running water, sinks,

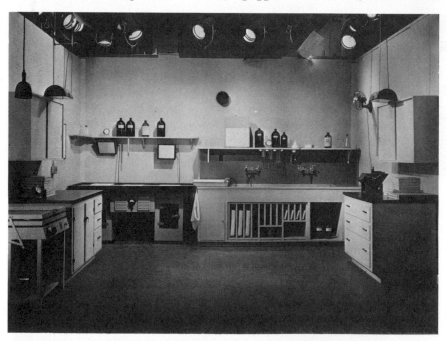

Fig. 3–1. A well-planned and equipped darkroom. (Reproduced, with permission, from *Kodak Data Book: Darkroom Construction for Professional, Photomechanical, and Industrial Use.*)

electric outlets, and storage cupboards for photographic paper and chemicals. It should be furnished with trays, film developers, driers, a clock timer, contact printer, and enlarging and rectifying cameras, depending upon the needs of the organization.

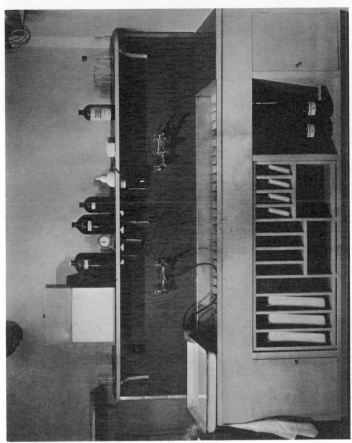

Fig. 3–3. Close-up view of processing sink. Notice the racks for graduates, extra electric outlets, and easily cleaned tray storage. (Reproduced, with permission, from *Kodak Data Book: Darkroom Construction for Professional, Photomechanical, and Industrial Use.*)

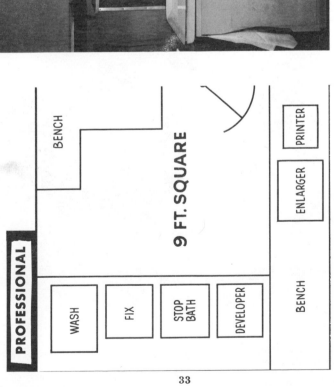

Fig. 3–2. Typical floor plan for a darkroom. (Reproduced, with permission, from *Kodak Data Book: Darkroom Construction for Professional, Photomechanical, and Industrial Use.*)

33

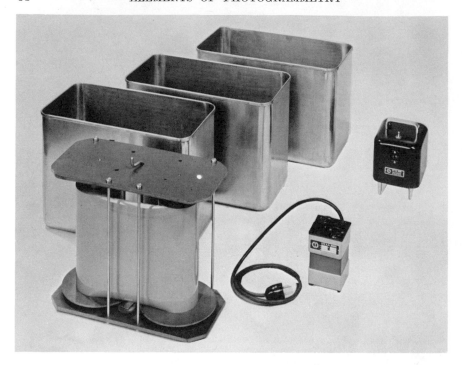

FIG. 3-4. Developing equipment for film (top) and for plates (bottom). (Courtesy of Wild Heerbrugg Instruments, Inc.)

3-3. The Negative. The light rays which are reflected from the ground surface to the aerial camera pass through the lens as the shutter opens and they are brought to a focus in the plane of the negative, which may be either a glass plate or a cellulose acetate film. The negative is coated with an emulsion consisting principally of silver bromide crystals, which have the property of being affected in proportion to the amount of light impinging upon them. Thus, the ground surface and objects upon it are registered in so far as they are marked by differences in light reflection. However, exposure alone does not show these variations, the "image" remaining latent until it is revealed through a process of development.

3-4. Development. To be developed, the film* is immersed in a liquid bath which reacts with the silver bromide crystals, changing them to black silver in proportion to the amount of light to which they have been exposed. If very little light reached a certain part of the negative, that part is darkened only slightly, while those parts struck by much light become very black. Thus light and dark areas on the negative are reversed from their appearance on the ground. The developing solution commonly consists of hydroquinone, sodium sulfate, potassium bromide, an alkali, a developing agent, and water.

To prevent overdevelopment, the film is removed at the proper time and immersed in a stop bath, consisting of dilute acetic acid, which washes off the remaining developer. From here it is placed in a third solution, called the fixative, which dissolves the undeveloped silver bromide. This fixing bath consists of sodium thiosulfate, sodium sulfite, acetic acid, potassium alum, an alkali, and water. Finally, the film is washed in clear water to remove traces of the previous solutions. Developing equipment for film and for plates is shown in Fig. 3-4.

When the film has been developed, it is dried either by hanging on racks in the air or by a special drying machine (Fig. 3-5). When dry, the film may be cut into individual negatives, each being placed in a folder for filing, or the roll may be left intact and rewound upon a spool.

3-5. Stamping. Each negative is stamped with a number for future identification. This can readily be done with a rubber stamp numberer (Figs. 3-6, 3-7) using black ink, the number on the positive then showing white. To obtain the correct reversal, the stamping is done on the "wrong" side of the negative. The identification material may consist of the roll number, photograph number, and commonly letter symbols to represent the particular project. The first and last pictures in a flight may also be lettered with the photographic scale and the contracting agency's initials. Furthermore, the date is shown on each photograph. This information is placed on one specified side (commonly the north), regardless of the direction in which the flight was made, and close to the edge to keep the obstruction of images to a minimum.

* The process for film is described, since it is more widely used than plates.

FIG. 3–5. Drying equipment for film. (Courtesy of Wild Heerbrugg Instruments, Inc.)

3–6. Contact Prints. Positive prints are made from the negatives in a contact printer, one of which is shown in Fig. 3–8. The roll is placed on a spindle at one side of the frame, and the film is stretched across the printing plate to a take-up spool on the opposite side. The photographic paper is then placed over the film, and the exposure is made by closing the top of the printer. Light passing through the negative strikes the emulsion of the sensitized paper. Dark places on the negative retard the light so that these are little affected and, when acted upon by the developer, leave a light spot on the print. The opposite, of course, holds for light places on the negative,

Fig. 3–6. Film marking kit. (Photo from files of Gordon Enterprises.)

so that the positive has the same gradations of light and dark that were on the ground when the photograph was taken. After the desired number of prints have been taken from one negative, the roll is wound to bring the next one into position for printing. The exposed positive prints are passed successively through the developer, stop bath, fixative, and wash water, and then hung to dry.

There are various weights and kinds of printing papers, including single and double weight and glossy, matte, and semimatte surfaces. The single weight is suitable for ordinary uses, but for mapping purposes, where distortion must be kept at a minimum, only the double weight should be used. For mapping, a dull finish such as that obtained with matte or semi-matte paper is common, while a glossy surface may be desired for display purposes or for mosaics.

3–7. Inspection. After a set of contact prints has been made, the photography as a whole may be inspected. Some inspection, as for quality of photography and presence of clouds or cloud shadows, can be made directly with the negatives, but checking for longitudinal and lateral overlaps,

FIG. 3–7. Film identification stamping machine. (Photo from files of Gordon Enterprises.)

coverage of the area, and excessive tilts can be done better with the contact prints.

3–8. Enlarging and Reducing. If it is desired to make a print at some specified enlargement or reduction ratio, an enlarger is used. After the negative is placed in a holder, a light source projects it through the lens to the printing table, the distances being such that the relation

$$\frac{1}{\text{object distance}} + \frac{1}{\text{image distance}} = \frac{1}{\text{focal length}}$$

is satisfied for perfect focus of the image. Photographic paper placed on the printing table may then be exposed at the desired ratio.

In the straight enlarger, the planes of the negative and positive are parallel so there is a change in size only and not in the angular characteristics of the picture. In a rectifying camera, the two holders may be tilted with

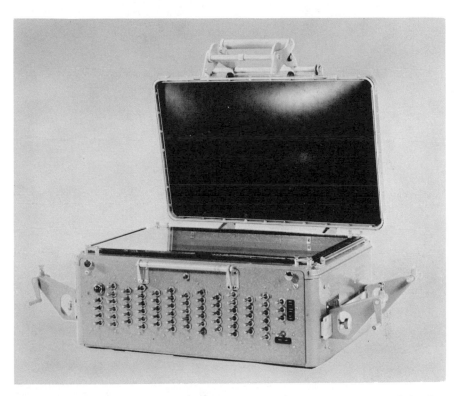

FIG. 3–8. Contact printer with pneumatic platen. (Photo from files of Gordon Enterprises.)

respect to each other. This allows a positive corresponding to a truly vertical photograph to be made from a tilted negative.

Photo-Indexes and Mosaics

3–9. Definitions. The photo-index and mosaic are considered together because of their similarity in construction and appearance. A photo-index is a photograph of an assemblage of the individual photographs of the area which shows their relative positions but with little attempt at an accurate matching of images between photographs except for the most prominent features. A mosaic is a photograph of an assemblage of the individual

FIG. 3–9. Example of a photo-index. (Courtesy of Jack Ammann Photogrammetric Engineers, Inc.)

pictures cut and fitted so that images from one photograph to the next match as closely as possible.

3–10. Uses of the Photo-Index. The photo-index (Fig. 3–9) serves two main purposes. First, it shows the relative location of photographs, with the number sequence indicating the direction of flight, and the photographs that adjoin a given photograph in any direction. Secondly, the index shows the photograph or photographs which cover any given area or feature of the terrain. While the size of the individual photograph is reduced to perhaps one-fourth that of the original print, it is still large enough so that the distinctive features can be recognized.

3–11. Photo-Index Construction. Single-weight prints can be used for making the lay-down of the index, since distortion is not a serious factor. For mounting, a piece of wallboard is used of sufficient size to contain the photographs for the area to be shown on the finished index. For example, if an index sheet 18 by 24 inches is desired and the ratio of reduction is to be 1 to 4, a mounting board of about 6 by 8 feet would be necessary. The board must be movable to allow positioning in the reproduction camera.

In constructing the index (Fig. 3–10), probably the best procedure is to lay one of the central flight strips of the area first, taking care that the

FIG. 3–10. Construction of photo-indexes. (Courtesy of Jack Ammann Photogrammetric Engineers, Inc.)

Fig. 3–11. A controlled mosaic. The matching of individual photographs is not readily apparent, except along the river. (Courtesy of Jack Ammann Photogrammetric Engineers, Inc.)

number of each photograph remains visible and that prominent line features such as main highways and rivers match with reasonable closeness. Some displacement of images is inevitable, but it can usually be reduced to an amount that will not be objectionable to the user.

Proceeding both ways from this central strip, one may then lay the adjoining strips, again keeping the photograph numbers visible and matching the more prominent images both within the flight and with the adjacent flight. If the photograph numbers are in the upper-right corners, the flights laid on the right must be inserted beneath those to the left to avoid covering the numbers of photographs already in place. For this reason, some may prefer to begin with the extreme right-hand flight and proceed to the left. However, this allows only one flight to be laid at a time, whereas two can be laid by the first method. Wire staples can be used to fasten the photographs to the board.

3–12. Finishing. After all the photographs have been securely fastened in place, a few operations remain to complete the index. Usually the number of the photograph at the end of each flight and sometimes that of each fifth photograph within the flight is emphasized by stick-up letters, since the photograph numbers themselves commonly do not reproduce plainly enough for quick discernment. Boundary lines of the flight area are marked, and a suitable title and north arrow placed in specified or convenient locations on the board. The whole assembly is then photographed at the desired reduction, after which the photographs may be dismounted.

3–13. Kinds of Mosaics. Mosaics may be either uncontrolled or controlled. For an uncontrolled mosaic, the photographs are laid with only the images on the photographs themselves as a guide. This is therefore somewhat like a photo-index, with exceptions that will later be apparent. In a controlled mosaic (Fig. 3–11), points located by ground surveying are identified on the photographs. These points are then plotted to the desired scale on the mounting board and the corresponding photograph points made to coincide with them as the photographs are laid.

3–14. Rectification. While the contact prints themselves may be used, often a better result can be had by enlarging or reducing the photographs so that the control points appearing on them fit as nearly as possible to their plotted positions on the board. As was shown in Article 2–11, the scale of a photograph is not constant but varies with the elevation of the ground. However, by a simple ratio of projection, two control points can be made to fit and, if relative tilt is introduced (as by means of a tilting easel or a rectifying camera), three points can be brought to coincide. For four or more points, some approximation of fitting or even a small warping of the print may be required.

If control is sparse, so that only a few photographs are rigidly fixed, one can lay the intermediate photographs, matching images carefully, starting at one of the controlled photographs and working toward the next. From the discrepancy in the location of corresponding images when this next controlled photograph is reached, a factor of enlargement or reduction can be calculated for the photographs of the flight strip as a whole.

3–15. Mosaic Construction. In the photo-index, the entire photograph is used. In mosaic construction, however, only the central portion is employed—this part being subject to least film and print distortion and to smallest displacements of images because of elevation of the ground features. The photographs must therefore be cut. While vertical cuts and butt joints might provide a smoother surface, they would be difficult to locate in order to obtain the best matching of images and to avoid gaps or overlaps. A better procedure is to leave the bottom photograph a little larger than necessary and to cut the top photograph obliquely to a feather edge so that it will lie over the other with no serious "bump." Practice with a safety-razor blade will soon enable one to make these feather edges deftly. To lessen the

FIG. 3–12. Setting a photograph in mosaic construction. (Courtesy of Jack Ammann Photogrammetric Engineers, Inc.)

unwelcome appearance of unmatched images, it is suggested that these cuts be made across areas having indefinite features, such as fields or woods, rather than along such prominent features as roads or rivers. A mosaic under construction is shown in Fig. 3–12.

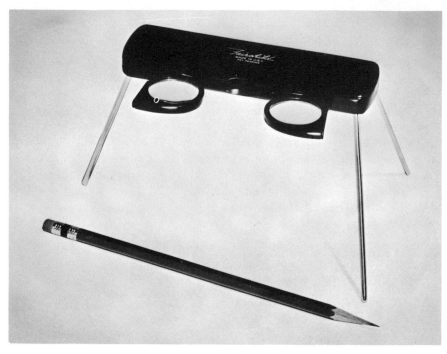

FIG. 3–13. Folding pocket-type stereoscope. (Courtesy of Fairchild Camera & Instrument Corporation.)

FIG. 3–14. Abrams Model CB-1 folding stereoscope. (Photo from files of Gordon Enterprises.)

Not only can the original photographs be changed in size for a better fit, but they can also be altered in tone or contrast for better matching in that respect, so that the junction between photographs will be less apparent. In a well-constructed mosaic, the lines between photographs are often discernible only upon careful scrutiny.

In an uncontrolled mosaic, there are no ground points to be plotted. Some measure of control can be obtained from features appearing in the photographs themselves, such as railroad lines, highways, transmission lines, and political or private boundary lines that are known to be straight. Otherwise, the parts of the photographs are laid with the matching of images being the main consideration in so far as their locations are concerned. It may be remarked that, since the placement of each photograph is less confined, the appearance of the uncontrolled mosaic from the standpoint of image matching may be somewhat superior to that of the controlled mosaic. This better appearance has been gained, of course, at the expense of accuracy of location.

The photographs for the mosaic are commonly fastened to the mounting board with rubber cement, since staples would not only be unsightly but would also leave the thin edges unprotected. The mosaic may be used in its original form or it may be rephotographed, as is the photo-index.

3–16. Uses of the Mosaic. The photo-index and the mosaic serve entirely different functions. The mosaic, in providing a composite picture of the area, does not give photograph numbers; in fact, it is highly desirable to avoid any appearance of individual photographs. While having some of the characteristics of one, a mosaic is not a true map any more than are the photographs from which it is made. The mosaic can be depended upon only for approximate scale, although the over-all scale of a controlled mosaic may be fairly accurately determined. The mosaic may show communities, roads, fields, and wooded areas to better advantage than a map. It probably provides more information to the general public than does the conventional map, although not as accurately from the engineering standpoint. It undoubtedly has its place in influencing public opinion and advancing public information in connection with existing conditions and proposed improvements.

Use of Stereoscope

3–17. Description. Since the simple viewing stereoscope is an invaluable aid in working with aerial photographs, a brief description of this instrument and directions for its use are given here. A more thorough discussion of the theory of the stereoscope and its use as a measuring instrument is found in Chapter 7.

The common portable or pocket stereoscope (Figs. 3–13, 3–14) consists of a frame holding two lenses of rather low magnification, their distance apart being adjustable to the user's eyes. Attached to the frame are two folding supports which, when in position for use, hold the lenses perhaps 3 to 4 inches from the table top. It will be recalled from Chapter 2 that aerial photographs are taken with about 60 per cent overlap. The stereoscope is used with a pair of these overlapping photographs so that one eye views the area in one photograph while the other eye views the corresponding area of the second photograph. Thus each eye sees the same area but from different viewpoints, namely, those of the camera in space at which the photographs were exposed. In effect, the observer's eyes are at these widely separated points, thus providing an exaggerated concept of the third dimension. It may readily be appreciated how valuable it is in photographic interpretation to have hills and buildings not only appear to rise from the photograph but seemingly to extend upward several times their normal height.

3–18. Orientation. The photographs are placed under the stereoscope in a prescribed relative position. For precise measurements, this alignment must receive careful attention, but for general viewing it need be only approximate.

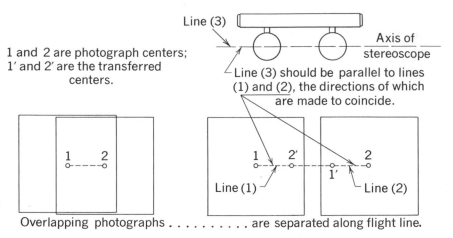

FIG. 3–15. Alignment of photographs and stereoscope. For small instruments the separated photographs will partially overlap.

In the orientation, three lines ought to be considered (Fig. 3–15, 3–16): (1) on photograph 1 from its center toward the center of photograph 2; (2) on photograph 2 from its center toward the center of photograph 1; and (3) the axis of the stereoscope, or the line connecting the centers of the two lenses. The photographs are placed so that the first two lines coincide in direction; the stereoscope axis is then brought parallel to them. Furthermore, corresponding images on the two photographs should be a distance apart roughly equal to the distance between the centers of the lenses which, in turn, is equal to the distance between the viewer's eyes, or eye base. A quick way of doing this is to lay one photograph over the other so that their common areas

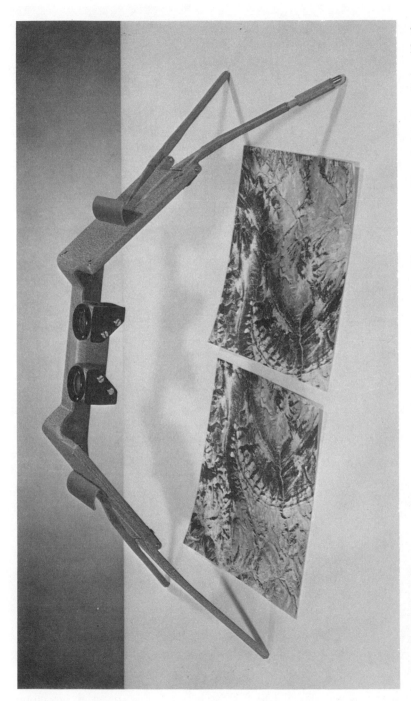

Fig. 3-16. Mirror-type stereoscope, showing correct orientation of photographs. Here they are separated farther than with the pocket type of instrument. (Courtesy of Fairchild Camera & Instrument Corporation.)

FIG. 3–17. A photograph pair set for viewing with a pocket-type stereoscope. (Photography by Commodity Stabilization Service, U. S. Department of Agriculture.)

approximately match. This can be done by rapidly flipping the top photo-graph up and down, bending it slightly near the center, and moving one of the photographs until corresponding images on the two photographs have no relative motion. Then the photographs are drawn apart in the direction of the line between their centers a distance roughly equal to the eye base, say $2\frac{1}{2}$ inches. The stereoscope is placed over the photographs with its axis parallel to the "line of centers" of the photographs. With small adjustments of the photographs, corresponding images as viewed by the eyes separately should eventually fuse into a single image in which the third dimension becomes strikingly noticeable. Some practice can be gained by looking stereoscopically at the photograph pairs in Fig. 3–17. It may take considerable time and patience to achieve complete fusion and a sense of the third dimension, but the results are so rewarding that no effort should be spared in its mastery, not alone for the aid it will provide in the interpretation of photographs but because the principle of the stereoscope underlies many of the methods and instruments used in mapping from aerial photographs.

LABORATORY PROBLEMS

Lab. Prob. 3–1. Construct a mosaic from one or more flight strips of contact prints. If the negatives and sufficient laboratory equipment are available, try rectifying the photographs to afford better matching both in scale and tone. Add place names, boundary lines, and other pertinent information in white ink and letter a title and a north arrow.

Lab. Prob. 3–2. The importance of practice in stereoscopic viewing can hardly be overestimated. A stereoscope and several pairs of overlapping photographs should be made available to each student. Orient each pair carefully, adjusting the photographs and instrument until good stereoscopic vision is obtained through-out the overlapping area. Persist until the third dimension is readily apparent. Mark the high points and the low points, the ridges and the valleys. Compare results with the Geological Survey quadrangle or another topographic map, if available.

4

INTERPRETATION AND CONTROL

4–1. Definitions. Interpretation is a study of the photograph to learn the nature of ground objects which the various images represent. The further determination of the particular objects on the ground is identification. The former would tell, for example, that some given image may be that of a tree, while the latter would determine that specific tree on the ground.

4–2. Uses. Both procedures are essential in photogrammetric work. If the photographs are to be used for mapping or surveying, at least a few points must be determined on both photograph and ground so that the former may be correctly oriented. Then, in the subsequent detailing operations, it is necessary to determine what the many photographic images represent on the ground so that they can properly be designated after transfer to the map.

The interpretation of an aerial photograph will largely depend upon its use. To the mapper, a wooded area is important because he must show it on his map by the appropriate symbols. A forester, however, might be interested in the kind of trees, their density, height, size, etc. The mapper will consider ground formations as problems in contouring, while to the geologist they may reveal the possibility of underground metallic deposits. Thus, each user of photographs will encounter his own peculiar problems and will develop his own methods and techniques.

4–3. Plan View. In general, a person looking at a vertical aerial photograph (Figs. 4–1, 4–2) obtains nearly the same view as if he were looking downward from a point above the ground. His view of images toward the edges of the photograph will be somewhat oblique, but this is not usually pronounced and is noticeable only for objects having a considerable height above ground level, such as tall buildings or smokestacks. Because it so closely resembles a plan view, the photograph is similar to a map. This may be an advantage to one familiar with maps, but it may at first be troublesome to those who are more accustomed to visualizing objects as seen from the ground.

4–4. Effect of Scale. The ease with which images may be recognized will also depend upon the scale of the photograph. For example, buildings in large-scale photography will be readily apparent by their definite rectangular outlines, while at smaller scales they may sometimes be confused with other

FIG. 4–1. Aerial photograph of a rural area. Note the varying shades of the water surfaces, the different appearances of wooded areas and fields, the hydroelectric station with its radiating power lines, and the railroad grade along the river. Scale is about 1:20,000. (Photography by Commodity Stabilization Service, U. S. Department of Agriculture.)

Fɪɢ. 4–2. Aerial photograph of urbanized area. Note the regular alignment of improved highways, the railroads along the river, the lock and dam, and the drive-in theater at the left. Scale is about 1 : 20,000. (Photography by Commodity Stabilization Service, U. S. Department of Agriculture.)

objects that are nearly but not exactly rectangular. Thus, in a farming area it might at first be difficult to distinguish between a barn and a haystack. Where both buildings and trees are close together, it may be difficult to tell the limits of each.

Objects which appear as lines, such as roads, railroads, sidewalks, and streams, are usually not difficult to interpret. Although portions of them may be obscured by trees, there is usually sufficient continuity to make them readily recognizable. They possess the advantage of having a long dimension in one direction, although perhaps very short in the other. Thus a narrow sidewalk can readily be seen, while a small shed of the same width may be invisible.

4–5. Appearance of Common Objects. The appearance of a road may depend more upon the nature of its surface than upon its importance and the amount of traffic served. Often a graded but unpaved road shows more prominently on the photograph than a black, paved highway. However, improved roads can usually be distinguished by their more regular alignment and curvature.

Railroads, especially if single-tracked, are not usually as prominent as roads or highways, but they have the characteristics of straight lines connected with uniform curvature. Aside from this, their darker appearance and narrowness often make them somewhat more difficult to trace than roads.

Individual towers of power transmission lines can usually be readily seen on the photographs, but pole lines may be more difficult to recognize. However, their paths through wooded country are easily discernible because of the cleared rights of way.

Bodies of water offer little difficulty if they are wide enough so that the individual banks can be distinguished. Water in the photograph may vary considerably from dark to light, depending upon the relative positions of sun, water, and camera. A small stream may be difficult to trace on the photograph, especially where it runs through a wooded area. For the accurate delineation of such drainage features, a stereoscope is not only helpful but almost a necessity.

Wooded areas are not usually difficult to recognize, but lone trees may be confused with haystacks, buildings, or other similar objects. A deciduous tree has an irregular pattern and is fairly light in color, while a conifer is more regular and dark. The appearance of a field will depend largely upon the time of year and the kind of vegetation. At large scales, row crops may be distinguished by their characteristic pattern, in contrast to fields of hay or grain. Freshly plowed fields are generally light in color.

4–6. Topographic Features. It may be well to note that topographical features are not readily interpreted from an inspection of a *single* aerial photograph, except as they may be inferred from the characteristic patterns of other features, such as drainage or roads. For example, a winding road may be following the meanders of a stream valley or climbing over a series of hills. The relief immediately becomes apparent with the stereoscopic viewing of two overlapping photographs.

4–7. Shadows. Since clear days are necessary for aerial photography, shadows of ground objects are inevitable. While they often tend to obscure other details or cause confusion with the objects themselves (Fig. 4–3), they are not altogether harmful, as will be pointed out presently.

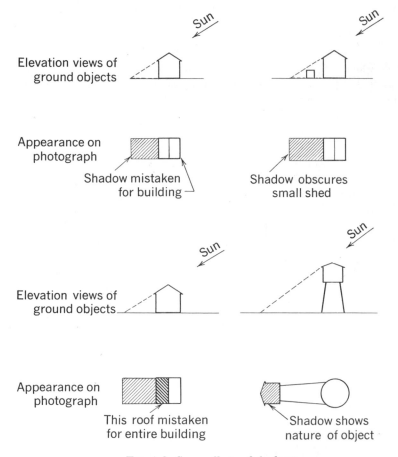

FIG. 4–3. Some effects of shadows.

The shadow of one object may partially or wholly obscure another as, for example, that of a row of trees across a sidewalk. The shadow may sometimes be confused with the object casting it, such as the dark shadow of a building with a light-colored roof. The prominent shadow may resemble the building which itself is almost invisible in the photograph because of its light color. The same situation may occur with trees, haystacks, and similar objects. Confusion may also occur with a gable-type roof where one side, sloping toward the sun, is reflected bright, while the other side is reflected dark. The latter is seen more distinctly and is often assumed to be the entire roof instead of only half of it. Thus, a point picked at one corner may in reality be at the ridge, while a point supposedly at the ridge is actually halfway down the slope.

Shadows may be helpful, however, if care is used in observation. In effect, they provide an elevation view of the object which is seen directly only in plan. This may be useful in determining the nature of the object itself. Thus, from their images only it may be difficult to distinguish a haystack from a large deciduous tree, but the characteristic shadow of each may reveal its identity. Shadows of bridges are often helpful in identifying the type of structure, not always evident from a top view.

In "reading" an aerial photograph, one must always keep in mind that shadows are present, and be careful not to mistake them for something else, at the same time taking full advantage of whatever help they may afford.

4–8. Control Points. In most photogrammetric work, at least a few points must be selected whose images on the photograph can be positively identified with their corresponding objects on the ground. This is to provide "control" for the photographs in order to orient them with respect to a ground survey. Points on the survey itself, or others which can readily be connected to the survey, provide such control.*

4–9. Selection of Points. Usually the photograph itself presents the limitation on point selection. That is, a point chosen on the photograph can be found on the ground more dependably than can a given ground point be spotted on the photograph. Also, it is often desirable that a point be chosen in a prescribed area of the photograph. Therefore the best procedure is to study the picture in the general desired location and select what seems to be a suitable point (Fig. 4–4). The photograph is then held correctly oriented and the corresponding point identified precisely on the ground. If identification is impossible or at all questionable, another point should be selected.

It is usually preferable to pick points at or not far above the ground level. This lessens the possibility of confusion with shadow, reduces the displacement of the image on the photograph, usually provides easier connection to the ground survey, and affords a superior view of the point from a position on the ground. However, sharp points not at ground level, such as roof gables, are not to be dismissed from consideration if better ones are unavailable. It is best to avoid trees, although a small conifer is not too objectionable. Excellent points are provided by intersections of sidewalks or roads, especially if they are narrow and well defined, small grass plots at intersections, and deck railroad bridges. These and similar objects are at ground level and small enough to form clear points if not obscured by trees or shadows.

* Ground control is discussed later in this chapter.

Fence corners, if distinct, provide good points, their height usually being insufficient to cause difficulty in identification and marking.

It is advisable to select unique points, if possible, in order to lessen the chance of mistakes in marking the photograph as well as to avoid ambiguities of description and possible misinterpretations by the field party in making the survey connections. Thus centers of roads or walks at an intersection are picked in preference to the sides, centers rather than corners of bridges, and gables instead of corners of buildings.

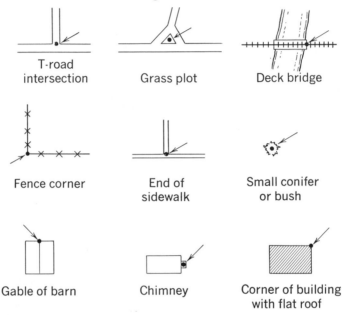

FIG. 4–4. Some possible ground control points.

4–10. Marking. When a point has finally been selected and identified, it is marked on the photograph by pricking the image with a fine needle, a magnifying glass being used with a single photograph or, preferably, a stereoscope with two photographs. This operation requires careful manipulation and considerable practice to achieve satisfactory results. The needle should be nearly perpendicular to the photograph so that its point will enter the emulsion squarely rather than at an oblique angle which would result in an elongated hole with a ragged edge (Fig. 4–5). The needle is pressed only through the emulsion, not through the entire thickness of the photograph, and the hole thus produced should be just large enough to be visible when the photograph is held to the light.

The needle may first be set at an angle to allow fuller vision of the image, lightly touching the photograph exactly at the point to be pricked. Then the needle is carefully raised to the perpendicular position and rotated by the

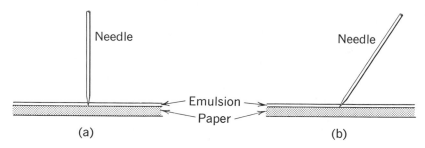

Fɪɢ. 4–5. Enlarged view of photograph and needle. (a) Holding the needle at right angles to the photograph gives a smooth round hole; (b) if the needle is held obliquely, the result is a rough elongated hole. Note that the needle pierces only the emulsion.

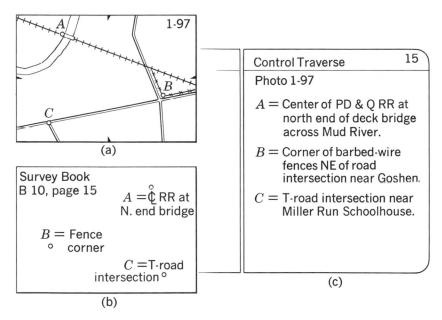

Fɪɢ. 4–6. (a) Face of photograph with control points A, B, and C. (b) Points marked on back of photograph. (c) Description of points in survey notebook.

fingers just enough to break the emulsion. The resulting hole is encircled with a pencil to mark its location. An identifying number or other designation is noted on the back of the photograph, together with a brief description of the point for the information of both the field survey party and the photogrammetrist (Fig. 4–6).

Ground Control

4–11. Need for Control. The impression may sometimes be given that aerial photography provides a method of surveying and mapping whereby all ground operations are eliminated. Except for the very roughest of work, this is by no means true, because the photographs must be oriented with respect to the ground before they can be correctly used in the mapping process. This orientation is achieved through points located by ground surveys. True, the ground work can be reduced to a very small amount, but it is erroneous to suppose that it can be eliminated entirely.

4–12. Control Defined. Essentially, ground control consists of a number of points on the earth whose images can be identified on the photographs and whose relative positions have been determined to the required accuracy by ground surveying methods. As is shown in a later chapter, it is possible to use the photographs themselves to locate additional points which will serve as subsidiary control. This photographic control should be distinguished from the ground control itself. However, it is commonly understood that the term *control*, when used alone, refers to points located by ground surveying. Horizontal control is needed for all kinds of mapping; in addition, vertical control is required for topographic maps as well as for certain other photogrammetric work. The kind of control and both the absolute and relative amounts of it vary widely with the nature of the work and the photogrammetric methods employed.

4–13. Methods. In general, ground control is furnished by conventional methods of surveying (Fig. 4–7) with which it is assumed the student is familiar. Therefore, only brief outlines of the procedures will be given, with special emphasis on any variations peculiar to their application in photogrammetry.

Horizontal control is established by traverse, triangulation, or a combination of the two. When laying out the traverse lines or setting the triangulation stations, it is preferable to have the photographs at hand so that the locations of control points can better be determined and the control thus more efficiently planned. Otherwise, expensive surveys may have their value materially lessened because they are not in the most advantageous location for controlling the photographs. Furthermore, definite control points can be selected and indicated both on the ground and on the photographs in advance so that the survey party can locate them as the line is run, thus saving return trips for corrections later. The photographs may also help the field party chief in selecting the most convenient routes for running his lines. It is to be realized, however, that delays in the delivery of photography and the desirability of providing work for the field crews may sometimes make it advisable to run control before the photographs are available.

4–14. Horizontal Control. Traverses are generally located along roads or railroads because they provide not only easier routes for taping but also a greater selection of suitable control points. Even in heavily wooded country there are always some identifiable points to be found along the roads, although by no means as frequently as in open areas. In extreme cases, however, in order to provide well-spaced points, it may be necessary to set some markers prior to the photographic flights. These may be of white cloth set in the form of a cross with arms measuring perhaps 3 feet by 10 feet, the dimensions being largely dependent upon the scale of the photography. Survey lines connect the markers to the ground traverse or triangulation scheme.

Fig. 4–7. Ground survey parties. (Courtesy of Air Survey Corporation.)

Traverses should close either on themselves or on points determined by surveys of higher accuracy. Since the aerial survey generally covers a fairly large area, the control commonly consists of triangulation of high order with traverses connecting the triangulation points. However, the possibility of employing triangulation for the secondary control in open, rolling terrain should not be overlooked. A possible disadvantage would be the necessity of entering private lands, since it would not normally be possible to establish all the stations on public roads. The accuracy of control should conform with standard specifications generally established for the corresponding control of maps produced by ground surveys (see Table 4–1). Fig. 4–8 shows a typical area with traverse control indicated in (a) and triangulation in (b).

4–15. Vertical Control. Vertical control consists of the elevations of various points throughout the area. These points may or may not be the

TABLE 4-1

RECOMMENDED SPECIFICATIONS FOR SMALL-SCALE CONTROL SURVEYS*

Order	Triangulation			Traverse			Levels	
	Length of Sight (mi.)	Average Error of Closure in Triangles	Probable Error in Base Measure	Length (mi.)	Maximum Error of Angles	Maximum Linear Error of Closure	Length of Circuit (mi.)	Maximum Error of Closure (ft.)
First	10–200	1"	$\frac{1}{1,000,000}$	50–500	2"	$\frac{1}{25,000}$	50–500	$0.017\ \sqrt{\text{miles}}$
Second	5–20	3"	$\frac{1}{500,000}$	25–200	5"	$\frac{1}{10,000}$	–	$0.035\ \sqrt{\text{miles}}$
Third	1–10	6"	$\frac{1}{250,000}$	10–100	30"	$\frac{1}{5000}$	10–100	$0.05\ \sqrt{\text{miles}}$
Fourth	$\frac{1}{2}$–2	1'	–	1–2	2'	$\frac{1}{1000}$	1–10	$0.1\ \text{to}\ 0.5\ \sqrt{\text{miles}}$

* Adapted, by permission, from R. E. Davis and F. S. Foote, *Surveying: Theory and Practice*, 4th ed. (New York: McGraw-Hill Book Co., Inc., 1953), p. 641.

same ones used for horizontal control, depending upon the methods employed in the photogrammetric work. In some cases, many more points are needed in elevation than in horizontal position. Methods of determining elevation include direct leveling with an engineer's level and rod, indirect leveling, stadia leveling, and the use of the aneroid barometer, depending upon the accuracy required (see Table 4–1). As in traversing, a line of levels should close either on itself or on points established by leveling of higher accuracy.

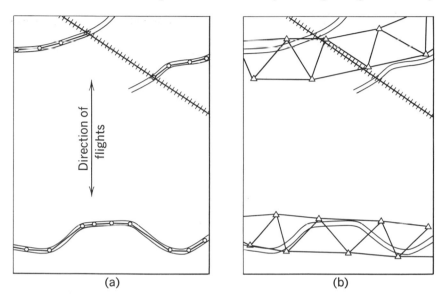

FIG. 4–8. Ground control (a) by traverses, (b) by triangulation.

4–16. Photograph Marking. Whether the control points are located as the traverse is run or later, it is important that they be identified on the photographs directly in the field. This procedure and the techniques of marking the photographs were described earlier in this chapter. The party chief should be provided with a convenient case for carrying a number of photographs, a small folding stereoscope, and a needle point. The case may also be designed to provide a sufficiently stiff support for holding two photographs in proper position for stereosocopic viewing.

After a point has been marked, the photograph is turned over and a brief description noted beside its location on the back, together with a reference to the field survey notes. The point should also be described and designated as a control point in the field survey notebook, with a reference given to the photograph on which the point was marked (Fig. 4–6).

4–17. Rectangular Coordinates. Either for plotting or for the calculation of positions, some method of rectangular coordinates is unquestionably the best. For a relatively small area in which the curvature of the earth is negligible, coordinates can readily be established on a local basis directly from the balanced latitudes and departures of the traverses or triangles. This is the method commonly presented in the elementary surveying texts in which total latitudes and total departures (or y- and x-coordinates) are computed with reference to axes commonly set through the southernmost and westernmost points, respectively, or in some other location if more convenient.

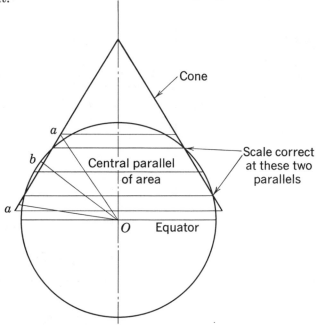

FIG. 4–9. Lambert conformal conic projection. The earth is projected outward to the cone at a, inward at b.

4–18. Geographic Coordinates. For larger areas, the curvature of the earth and the convergency of the meridian must be considered in plotting or in the calculation of position. Points on the earth's surface are located by latitude and longitude, by which values they can be plotted on a sheet laid off on a projection of meridional and latitudinal lines. For certain calculations, however, it may be necessary to transfer from this geographical system to a plane coordinate system in some linear unit. This transformation can be accomplished with the aid of tables prepared by the U. S. Coast and Geodetic Survey and available in Special Publication No. 71 entitled *Relation Between Plane Rectangular Coordinates and Geographic Positions*.

4–19. State Coordinate Systems. Because of their convenience for the practicing surveyor, systems of plane coordinates for the several states have been developed by the U. S. Coast and Geodetic Survey. Again, because of the earth's curvature, coordinates of a point based on a plane surface will gradually depart from those of a spherical surface as the point recedes from the origin. By a careful location of the plane with respect to the earth's surface, and confining it to only a portion of the state if necessary, the maximum discrepancy is kept to less than 1 in 10,000. Thus the larger states may have more than one region or system. Either a Lambert conformal conic or a transverse Mercator projection is used, depending upon whether the area extends predominantly east-west or north-south, respectively.

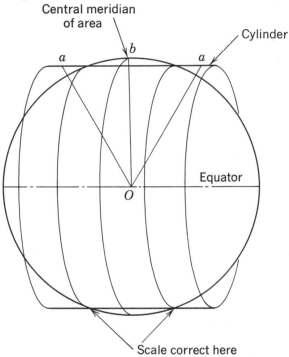

FIG. 4–10. Transverse Mercator projection. The earth is projected outward to the cylinder at a, inward at b.

4–20. Lambert Projection. While these projections and the coordinates based upon them are actually determined by mathematical analysis, they can be readily illustrated by graphical means. The Lambert projection (Fig. 4–9) is based on an imaginary cone intersecting the earth's surface in two parallels of latitude, which lie about equidistant from the center of the area covered by the plane coordinate system. Points on the earth's surface are projected outward or inward upon the cone by lines radiating from a central point practically at the earth's center, and the conical surface is then unrolled into a plane.

4–21. Transverse Mercator Projection. The transverse Mercator projection (Fig. 4–10) is formed by a cylinder whose axis is in the plane of the earth's equator and which intersects the earth along two circles parallel to the central meridian of the area. Here also the projection from earth to cylinder radiates from a point near the earth's center, after which the cylinder is unrolled into a plane. It will thus be seen that the plane will be at true scale only along the two lines in either projection where the cone or cylinder intersects the earth's surface. Toward the center of the area from these, the scale of the plane will be too small, while in the outer portions it will be too large.

4–22. Use of State Coordinates. Locations of the numerous monuments set by the governmental surveying and mapping agencies can be expressed in the plane coordinate system, and these can then be used by any surveyor or engineer as he may require. These stations can thus serve as control or check points of a relatively high degree of accuracy based upon a system of simple plane coordinates rather than geographical coordinates, which are relatively more difficult to use. The necessary computations are illustrated in U. S. Coast and Geodetic Special Publication No. 235, *The State Coordinate Systems (A Manual for Surveyors)*.

LABORATORY PROBLEM

Lab. Prob. 4–1. If they are available, photographs of a nearby area should be used so that field identifications can be made. With a needle, mark several points on the photographs which can be positively identified on the ground. Describe each briefly on the back of the photograph. Determine as many different features on the photographs as possible: paved and unpaved roads, railroads, streams, transmission lines, fences, buildings, and so forth, and compare these with the corresponding objects on the ground. If necessary, use the U. S. Geological Survey quadrangle sheets instead of making a trip to the field, although this is no substitute for actual point identification which must be done on the ground.

5

VERTICAL PHOTOGRAPHS

5–1. Definition. A vertical aerial photograph is one for which the axis of the camera is maintained as closely as possible in a truly vertical position. Thus the photograph itself, being perpendicular to the camera axis, lies approximately in a horizontal plane. This type comprises the bulk of aerial photography for mapping and probably presents the most satisfactory approach to the fundamentals of photogrammetry.

5–2. Principles. Fig. 5–1 shows, in simplified form, the light reflected

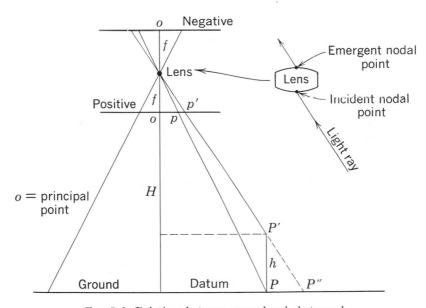

FIG. 5–1. Relations between ground and photograph.

from ground objects, passing through the camera lens, and coming to a focus in the plane of the negative. No attempt has been made to indicate either the complex structure of the lens or the actual paths of the light rays through it. From optical theory, it is known that the light ray emerging from a certain point (emergent nodal point) on the upper side of the lens is parallel to the corresponding ray entering a certain point (incident nodal point) on the lower side, regardless of its deviations as it passes through the lens (see Art. 2–7). The result of the light upon the film is a negative picture, that is, reversed both in position and in shape with respect to the corresponding ground objects. A positive picture, which is more convenient to consider and which is normally used, is represented below the lens.

In aerial photography, the distance of the camera above the ground, even at fairly low altitudes, is always very large in comparison with the focal length. Therefore, if the object distance is taken to be infinite in the optical relation,

$$1/\text{object distance} + 1/\text{image distance} = 1/\text{focal length}$$

it will be seen that, for practical purposes, image distance is equal to the focal length, which accordingly will be considered as the perpendicular distance from the lens to the photograph. The foot of this perpendicular on the photograph is called the *principal point* and is commonly considered as the origin for the measurement of coordinates of points with respect to axes parallel to the edges of the photograph.

5–3. Nadir Point. The photograph point corresponding to the point on the ground vertically beneath the camera at the time of exposure is called its *nadir point*. If the ideal situation obtained wherein the camera axis were exactly vertical, the nadir and principal points would coincide. Since this is seldom attainable in practice, the nadir point is ordinarily at some other position, as shown in Fig. 5–2.

5–4. Relief Displacements. The variation in the scale of a vertical photograph caused by a change in ground elevation was treated earlier in Chapter 2. The effect of elevation upon the image itself will now be considered. Referring again to Fig. 5–1, note that as P moves vertically through the height h, its image on the photograph moves from p to p'. Since op and op' coincide in direction, it may be stated that the image displacement caused by topographic relief radiates from the center of the photograph, outward for points lying above the datum and inward for points below it. This image "movement" is called a displacement or error merely for convenience in analysis, since obviously the images will appear on the photograph in accordance with the normal physical behavior of light. The displacement would be present even with a camera structurally and optically perfect, operating under ideal atmospheric conditions. It is true that errors in mapping may be introduced if no allowance is made for the effect of relief, and provisions for it must be included in any but the very roughest of map making.

By similar triangles (Fig. 5–1),

$$\frac{PP''}{H} = \frac{pp'}{f} \qquad \text{and} \qquad \frac{PP''}{h} = \frac{op'}{f}$$

So

$$PP'' \cdot f = pp' \cdot H = op' \cdot h$$

Hence

$$pp' = op' \cdot \frac{h}{H} \qquad (5\text{--}1)$$

where pp' = the relief displacement on the photograph

op' = the radial distance to the point from the center of the photograph

h = elevation of the point

H = flying height above datum

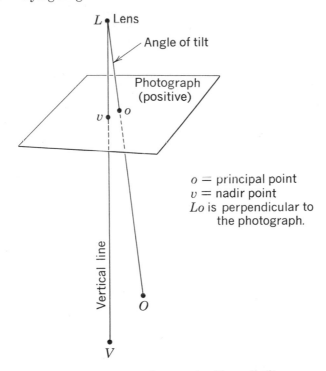

FIG. 5–2. Vertical photograph with small tilt.

EXAMPLE 5–1. Calculate the relief displacement for a point 4.38 in. from the center of the photograph taken at an altitude of 15,000 ft., the elevation of the point being 1800 ft.

$$\text{Displacement} = \frac{4.38 \times 1,800}{15,000} = 0.526 \text{ in.}$$

Scale Checking

5–5. Photograph Scale. It has previously been shown that a vertical aerial photograph has no uniform scale if the ground surface is of varying elevation (Art. 2–11). It has also been shown that the image of any point on the photograph may be considered as "displaced" along a radial line from the center as a result of its elevation (Art. 5–4). It follows that if all points could be corrected for elevation displacement, the result would be a photograph having a common scale throughout. If this scale were determined, the photograph could then be used with the utmost propriety for scaling directions and distances. It is obviously unnecessary that the photograph in its entirety be thus "reduced" to a common scale; it is sufficient to correct individual points as they are needed.

5–6. Scale Checking. The process of determining the scale of a vertical photograph for points at a specified elevation and the subsequent measurement of directions and distances therefrom is often called *scale checking*. This term may have developed from certain uses of photography requiring a specified scale; then procedures to determine how closely this scale had been attained could properly be called scale checking. Actually, the method is one of scale determination, regardless of any specification as to its value.

For the present discussion, the photograph will be considered as truly vertical. The extent to which scale is affected by tilt is shown in Chapter 8, and further elaborations of the scale-checking method are considered in Chapter 10.

5–7. Relief Displacements. In Art. 5–4, it was shown that the image displacement of a point on a vertical photograph due to relief is $d \cdot h/H$, where d is the radial distance from the center of the photograph, h is the

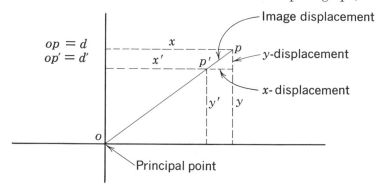

FIG. 5–3. Components of image displacement.

elevation of the point, and H is the flying height. If a point image is located by coordinates with respect to rectangular axes, then by similar triangles (Fig. 5–3),

$$x\text{-displacement} = x \cdot \frac{h}{H} \qquad \text{and} \qquad y\text{-displacement} = y \cdot \frac{h}{H}$$

which, applied to x and y, yield coordinates x' and y' reduced to the datum.

5–8. Control. It will be observed that the ground elevation of each desired point must be known. These elevations can be obtained from existing topographic maps, by leveling, by barometers, or by one of the photogrammetric methods discussed in subsequent chapters. It is also necessary that at least two of the points be known in horizontal position on the ground. If scale only and not directions are to be determined, the distance between two points will be sufficient.

5–9. Flying Height. Let AB represent a distance on the ground, and $a'b'$ the corresponding distance on the photograph after the elevation corrections for points a and b have been made. Then the scale (at datum) of the photograph may be calculated by $AB/a'b'$. However, to determine the corrections necessary to yield $a'b'$, the value of H must be known. From Art. 2–12,

$$H = \frac{AB}{a'b'} \cdot f$$

but this in turn presupposes that the value of $a'b'$ is known. An approximate value of H can be calculated from the uncorrected distance ab. If this is designated as (H), then

$$(H) = \frac{AB}{ab} \cdot f$$

plus the mean* of the elevation of A and B.

This value of (H) will often be sufficiently close for calculating the relief corrections $x \cdot h/(H)$ and $y \cdot h/(H)$ for the two points a and b. These corrections reduce the absolute values of the coordinates when the elevation is positive. From the trial-corrected distance $(a'b')$, a better value of (H) can be found. It should then be determined whether this new value will seriously alter the previously calculated relief displacements, and, if so, the procedure should be repeated. The scale of the photograph at datum is then $(H)/f$.

EXAMPLE 5–2. Following are the survey and photograph coordinates for two points, the camera focal length being 8.25 in. Determine the flying height H and the datum scale.

Point	X	Y	Elevation	Point	x	y
A	850 ft.	1025 ft.	500 ft.	a	−3.48 in.	−1.80 in.
B	4070 ft.	2135 ft.	800 ft.	b	+2.07 in.	+3.62 in.

The length of AB is $\sqrt{(3220)^2 + (1110)^2} = 3406$ ft.

* This value will not be exact unless A and B are symmetrically located with respect to the principal point (see Chapter 10).

The uncorrected length ab is $\sqrt{(5.55)^2 + (5.42)^2} = 7.76$ in.

$$\frac{3406 \times 8.25}{7.76} = 3621 \text{ ft.}$$

$$\frac{500 + 800}{2} = \underline{650}$$

$$H = 4271 \text{ ft.}$$

Point a: x-Correction $= \dfrac{500}{4271} \times 3.48 = 0.41$

y-Correction $= \dfrac{500}{4271} \times 1.80 = 0.21$

Point b: x-Correction $= \dfrac{800}{4271} \times 2.07 = 0.39$

y-Correction $= \dfrac{800}{4271} \times 3.62 = 0.68$

Point	x-Correction	y-Correction	x'	y'
a	0.41 in.	0.21 in.	−3.07 in.	−1.59 in.
b	0.39 in.	0.68 in.	+1.68 in.	+2.94 in.

The corrected length $a'b'$ is $\sqrt{(4.75)^2 + (4.53)^2} = 6.56$ in.

$$H = \frac{3406 \times 8.25}{6.56} = 4283 \text{ ft.}$$

This change from the original value (H) will make no appreciable change in the corrections.

$$\text{Datum scale} = \frac{H}{f} = \frac{4283}{8.25} = 519 \text{ ft./in.}$$

5–10. Graphical Method. If desired, a considerable part of the work can be done directly on the photograph or on tracing paper laid over it. In this case, radial lines from the center are drawn through the points and the displacement corrections laid off along these lines. The lengths ab and $a'b'$ can then be scaled directly. The relative directions of lines determined by the displaced points are correct and can be measured with a protractor.

If the lengths are to be determined by calculation, it is probably better to use coordinates and calculate the lengths and directions by ordinary surveying methods.

5–11. Distances. To determine the ground lengths of new lines, the photograph coordinates of the points are first corrected for elevation. Then the photograph distance, as calculated from these corrected coordinates, is multiplied by the known scale of the photograph to give the ground distance.

EXAMPLE 5–3. The following coordinates for points c and d are measured on the photograph of Example 5–2. Determine the ground distance CD.

Point	x	y	Elevation (from ground survey)
c	−2.76 in.	+3.94 in.	650 ft.
d	+3.08 in.	−0.72 in.	1120 ft.

Point c: x-Correction $= \dfrac{650}{4283} \times 2.76 = 0.42$

y-Correction $= \dfrac{650}{4283} \times 3.94 = 0.60$

Point d: x-Correction $= \dfrac{1120}{4283} \times 3.08 = 0.81$

y-Correction $= \dfrac{1120}{4283} \times 0.72 = 0.19$

Point	x-Correction	y-Correction	x'	y'
c	0.42 in.	0.60 in.	−2.34 in.	+3.34 in.
d	0.81 in.	0.19 in.	+2.27 in.	−0.53 in.

The length $c'd' = \sqrt{(4.61)^2 + (3.87)^2} = 6.02$ in.

Ground distance $CD = 6.02 \times 519 = 3124$ ft.

5–12. Directions. If azimuths or bearings are desired, the direction as well as the distance of the control line must be known from the ground survey. The azimuth of the control line on the photograph is determined with respect to one of the photograph axes. Then the difference between the photograph azimuth and the ground azimuth of the control line yields the correction that must be applied to all calculated photograph directions to give the corresponding ground directions. Thus the bearings and lengths of new lines, whether isolated or connected, can be determined.

EXAMPLE 5–4. Determine the bearing of CD of Example 5–3.

Tan azimuth $AB = \dfrac{3220}{1110} = 2.901$ Azimuth $AB = $ 70° 59′

Tan azimuth $a'b' = \dfrac{4.75}{4.53} = 1.049$ Azimuth $a'b' = $ 46° 22′

Correction $= $ 24° 37′

Tan azimuth $c'd' = \dfrac{4.61}{3.87} = 1.191$ Azimuth $c'd' = $ 130° 01′

Azimuth $CD = $ 154° 38′
Bearing $CD = $ S 25° 22′ E

5-13. Coordinate Method. Another and perhaps a preferred method is to work with points rather than lines, determining the ground coordinates of each point, from which the bearing and length of any desired line can readily be calculated. In this method, a control line is used as before to determine the scale and the azimuth correction. Then a second line from the center of the photograph to one of the control points serves to determine the ground coordinates of the photograph center. New points are located by direction and distance from the center, from which their ground coordinates can be computed.

EXAMPLE 5-5. Determine the bearing and length of CD of Example 5-3 by the coordinate method.

The photograph azimuth of each point is obtained from tan azimuth $= x'/y'$, and the distance of each point from the photograph center is given by $d' = \sqrt{(x')^2 + (y')^2}$. Values of the corrected coordinates x' and y' are taken from Examples 5-2 and 5-3.

Point	x'	y'	Tan Photo Azimuth	Photo Azimuth	d'
b	+1.68 in.	+2.94 in.	0.5714	29° 45′	3.39 in.
c	−2.34 in.	+3.34 in.	0.7006	324° 59′	4.08 in.
d	+2.27 in.	−0.53 in.	4.283	103° 09′	2.33 in.

The datum scale of the photograph was found in Example 5-2 to be 519 ft./in. and the azimuth correction (photograph to ground) was determined in Example 5-3 to be +24° 37′. Then the ground azimuth of any point from O equals the photograph azimuth plus 24° 37′ and the ground distance from O to the point is 519 d'.

Point	Ground Azimuth from O	Ground Distance	Sin Azimuth	Cos Azimuth	ΔX	ΔY
B	54° 22′	1759 ft.	0.8128	0.5826	+1430 ft.	+1025 ft.
C	349° 36′	2118 ft.	0.1805	0.9836	− 382 ft.	+2083 ft.
D	127° 46′	1209 ft.	0.7905	0.6125	+ 956 ft.	− 741 ft.

With the X- and Y-differences thus determined, the coordinates of O are calculated from those of the known point B and then, in turn, the coordinates of C and D are calculated from those of O.

Point	X	Y
B	4070 ft.	2135 ft.
O	2640 ft.	1110 ft.
C	2258 ft.	3193 ft.
D	3596 ft.	369 ft.

Length $CD = \sqrt{(1338)^2 + (2824)^2} = 3125$ ft.

Tan azimuth $CD = \dfrac{1338}{2824} = 0.4738$ Azimuth $CD = 154° \, 39'$

Bearing $CD = S \, 25° \, 21' \, E$

5–14. Area. The area of a figure determined by either of these procedures may be computed by regular surveying methods, either by coordinates or by double meridian distances. In some kinds of work, however, it may be sufficiently accurate and much more rapid to determine the area by planimetering directly upon the photograph, provided the boundaries of the desired area can be outlined thereon. In theory, every single point along the boundary line should be displaced according to its elevation. This, of course, would not be practicable. Instead, the area may be planimetered as it appears on the photograph and a correction applied to it depending upon the "average" elevation of the terrain along the boundaries. It should be noted that elevations inside the tract would have no effect on the area; only those along the boundary lines themselves are affected. Thus, if the boundary encircles the base of a hill, the elevation of the hill itself would not be of consequence. The photograph, if so desired, may be marked in zones of different elevations, each one representing a certain percentage correction to be applied to the measured area.

5–15. Slope. A precaution must be noted in determining an area whose boundary lines may be partly or wholly on steep slopes. As shown in Fig. 5–4, the photographed area of a sloping field will depend upon whether the

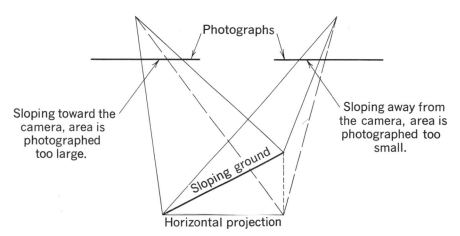

FIG. 5–4. Effect of slope on photographed area.

slope is toward or away from the center of the photograph. Neither will show the true value, even when corrected for an "average" elevation of the boundaries. If the area slopes toward the center, the field will be photographed too large; if the area slopes away from the center, the field will appear too small. The difference between the true and the apparent areas will increase with the distance from the center of the photograph, with the elevations, and with the steepness of slope. Suitable correction tables may be prepared, depending upon these three factors, or each area may be considered as an individual problem.

5–16. Summary. These scale-checking procedures present relatively simple methods of determining bearings, distances, and areas and, unlike many photogrammetric methods, use but a single photograph at a time. About the only equipment needed is an instrument for measuring coordinates or scaling distances directly on the photograph. For much work, a finely divided engineer's scale, carefully used, is satisfactory, while a planimeter is suitable for the direct determination of area from the photographs. Among the disadvantages of scale checking may be mentioned the need of elevations and the possibility of errors introduced by tilt.

PROBLEMS

5–1. Calculate the relief displacement for a point 3.74 in. from the center of a photograph, the flying height being 10,500 ft. and the elevation of the point being 2240 ft.

5–2. The image of a point whose elevation is 950 ft. is 54.67 mm. from the center of the photograph. What would this distance be if the point were at datum? $H = 12,000$ ft.

5–3. The image of a point that is 120 ft. below datum is 68.09 mm. from the center of the photograph. What would the distance be if the point were at datum? $H = 8400$ feet.

5–4. The image of a point at datum is 3.00 in. from the center of the photograph, H being 18,000 ft. What would the corresponding distance be if the elevation of the point were 1000 ft.? 2000 ft.? 5000 ft.?

5–5. What elevation would cause a relief displacement of 0.25 in. if the image is 4.62 in. from the center of the photograph, H being 16,500 ft.?

5–6. For what flying height would the relief displacement be 0.30 in. for a point whose image is 5.17 in. from the center of the photograph and whose elevation is 2720 ft.?

5–7. Calculate the flying height and datum scale for a photograph whose focal length is 8.250 in. if the survey and photograph coordinates of two points whose images appear upon the photograph are as follows:

Point	X (ft.)	Y (ft.)	Z (ft.)	x (in.)	y (in.)
A	1240	3075	1250	−1.472	+3.015
B	4460	4150	980	+3.308	−0.682

5–8. Determine the ground distance of the line 1—2 on the photograph of Prob. 5–7, using the method of Art. 5–11.

Point	x (in.)	y (in.)	Elevation (ft.)
1	−2.890	+1.024	1550
2	+3.074	+2.752	1810

5–9. Calculate the bearing of line 1—2 of Prob. 5–8, using the method of Art. 5–12.

5–10. Calculate the bearing and distance of line 3—4 on the photograph of Prob. 5–7, using the method of Arts. 5–11 and 5–12.

Point	x (in.)	y (in.)	Elevation (ft.)
3	+1.362	−1.804	750
4	−2.744	−2.005	1130

5–11. Calculate the bearings and distances of the traverse 1–2–3–4 of the above problems, using the method of Arts. 5–11 and 5–12.

5–12 through **5–15.** Same as Prob. 5–8 through 5–11, using the method of Art. 5–13.

5–16. Given the following survey and photograph coordinates on a photograph whose focal length is 150 mm.:

Point	X (ft.)	Y (ft.)	Z (ft.)	x (mm.)	y (mm.)
M	980	2630	1830	−48.62	−52.04
N	3620	1080	1280	+25.17	−17.45
11			925	+40.48	+48.63
12			1140	+62.10	+11.96
13			1565	+12.95	−50.37
14			2140	− 6.74	−19.80
15			1735	−36.02	+42.53

(a) Calculate the bearings and distances for the traverse 11–12–13–14–15, using the method of Arts. 5–11 and 5–12.

(b) Same as part (a), using the method of Art. 5–13.

LABORATORY PROBLEMS

Lab. Prob. 5–1. Determine the datum scale for one or more photographs for which ground control data are available. Then determine the bearing and distance of one or more new lines appearing on these photographs. It is desirable that some of these new values be known from ground measurements as a check.

6

RADIAL-LINE MAPPING

6–1. Photograph Control. It was stated in Chapter 4 that additional control points may be located from the photographs themselves. The radial-line control method* accomplishes this by utilizing lines radiating from the centers of the photographs. Although the method can be applied to obliques, its application to vertical photography only will be discussed in this chapter.

6–2. Requirements. The photographs must be taken according to the usually specified overlaps, about 60 per cent in the line of flight, and 25 to 30 per cent between adjacent flights. Tilts must be small, preferably less than 1 or 2 degrees. The large overlap in the line of flight is required because there must be some area common to three successive photographs, as will presently be shown. Incidentally, the stereoscopic views thus provided are very helpful, though perhaps not absolutely necessary.

6–3. General Principles. Directions only are taken from the photographs, no reliance being made at all upon scale, which, as has previously been demonstrated, varies with ground elevation. It was shown in Art. 5–4 that displacements of photographic images resulting from ground elevations are along lines radiating from the principal point. Therefore, ground elevation has no effect upon the radial direction of a point, and it follows that angles measured on the photograph at its center are correct in so far as any image displacements resulting from topographic relief are concerned. It is to be remembered that this is strictly true only for perfectly vertical photographs, but as long as tilts are not excessive, the errors introduced in the horizontal angles are usually negligible. Furthermore, it can be assumed that the tilts are random in both direction and amount and that the errors resulting therefrom may tend to compensate.

6–4. Outline of Method. In describing the method, a typical situation will be assumed in which there are several flight strips, each of which extends from one line of ground control across perhaps eight to ten photographs to a second line of control. This might be only a portion of a larger project, the

* The first extensive aerial surveys in the United States were done by radial control, this method having been used by the U. S. Forest Service in connection with its expanded land acquisition program, and by the Tennessee Valley Authority in mapping 42,000 square miles during the period 1933–38.

whole of which would consist of repetitions of this basic unit. Following is a brief outline of the method, after which the various steps are described in detail.

1. The photographs are marked to show the center points, the ground control points, and all the secondary (photographic) control points, which are those to be located by the radial-line control.
2. A templet is made for each photograph, upon which directions from the center to all other points on the picture are marked.
3. These templets are laid on a base sheet so that they fit together and also fit the ground control, which has previously been plotted on the sheet.
4. The photographic control points thus located are marked on the base sheet.

6–5. Center Point. The first step in preparing the photograph is to mark its center point. This is determined from the fiducial marks which are photographed directly upon each exposure, either along the edges or in the corners of the picture (see Fig. 6–1), the center being at the intersection of lines connecting opposite marks. Because of the 60 per cent overlap, the image at the center will appear on each of the two adjoining pictures and these "conjugate" centers must also be marked. The center of the photograph is a fixed point, and whether or not it coincides with any reasonably definite image is purely accidental. The transfer and marking of a conjugate center, however, does require some use of definite photographic images. While an experienced person can often mark the true conjugate center, there may be merit in picking some definite image near the true center as a substitute which can be more readily transferred. This substitute center need only be seen on the adjacent photographs and need not be identified nor even recognizable on the ground. Seldom will it be necessary to deviate more than one-eighth of an inch from the true center. While the use of a substitute center may introduce errors in photographic directions, it avoids the error attributable to the uncertain transfer of the true center. Furthermore, since there is unavoidably some tilt, the center of relief displacement is not exactly at the principal point. It would thus seem that the use of a substitute center, within certain limitations, is amply justified. In the following discussion, the word *center* refers to the point actually used, whether it be the true center or a substitute.

6–6. Photograph Marking. The centers and conjugate centers, as well as all subsequent points that are selected, must be marked on the photographs. This is commonly done with inked circles of different sizes and colors, as shown in Fig. 6–1, the centers of the circles of course being the points themselves.

Each ground control point must be marked on all the photographs upon which it appears, anywhere from two to possibly six, together with its designating letter or number.

Finally, in the preparation of the photographs, there is the selection and marking of the radial-line control points themselves. These consist of

Fig. 6–1. Aerial photograph with points marked for radial control. The small center and conjugate center points are in red; the photograph control points are in blue; and the ground control points, marked *A* and *B*, are in black. (Photography by Commodity Stabilization Service, U. S. Department of Agriculture.)

images which are clear and definite but which normally do not have to be identifiable on the ground. Thus, one of a number of small spots in an open field might provide an excellent point, yet be almost impossible to identify. These points are selected in the 20 per cent band across the central part of the photograph that is common to both adjacent pictures and are marked on all three of the photographs. The number of points selected in each band may vary, but three on each side of the center, well distributed across the photograph, are fairly common.

6–7. Templets. For the construction of the radial-line network, templets are used rather than the photographs themselves. Upon each templet, lines are established radiating from the center toward the conjugate centers and all other points that have been selected on the photograph. Three principal kinds of templets are in use: the transparent acetate templet, the opaque slotted templet, and the mechanical or metal-arm templet. All these utilize the same principles in assembly, the differences being in materials and methods of construction.

6–8. Construction of Templets. The use of the transparent templet is treated in full, because of its reasonable cost and its simplicity, with comments upon the differences for the other types. A sheet of acetate is placed over the photograph, centered, and fastened securely to it. A circle is drawn to mark the center, and radial lines are drawn from it through the conjugate centers which appear on the photograph, together with notations of their photograph numbers. Segments of radial lines are then drawn through the other points that have been marked on the photograph, those for ground control being labeled with their appropriate designations. The length and location of each of these segments depend upon the scale of the desired plot. Since directions only are taken from the photograph, its scale plays no part in the templet construction, and an enlargement or reduction may be effected as desired. All that is needed are line segments of such length and location that intersections are assured when the templets are laid.

Lines are drawn with ink as finely as possible. Were the material not to be reused for other sections or projects, the lines could be formed by scratching with a sharp knife or other scribing tool and then filled with ink. If the templets are to be used over again for different photographs as the work proceeds from one section to another, it is better to draw the lines with a closely set ruling pen. The ink may then be readily washed off when the templet is to be used for another photograph.

6–9. Laying the Templets. The first templet in a flight is laid so that the rays to the ground control points pass through corresponding points which have previously been plotted on the base sheet. To locate a single templet requires a minimum of three ground control points (Fig. 6–2). The next templet is then located by noting that its center lies along the line 1—2′ on the first templet, which has already been placed. Furthermore, the line 2—1′ on the second templet must coincide with 1—2′ on the first. No. 2 is then fixed in position by sliding it on top of No. 1, maintaining the above coincidence until the ray to a control point passes through that point. It will now be seen that rays to points common to templets 1 and 2 intersect to give the locations of new (photographic control) points. Some of these

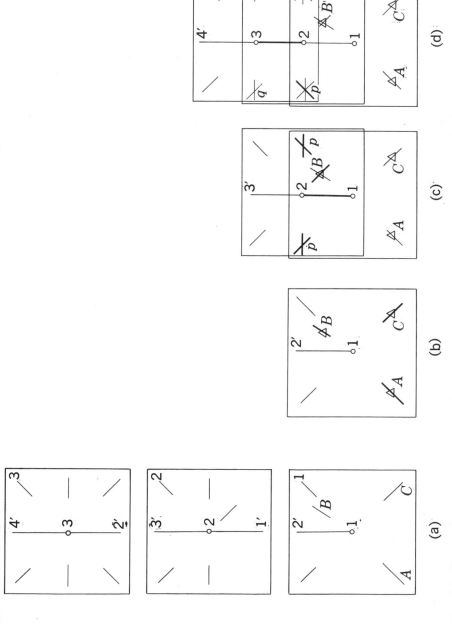

Fig. 6–2. How transparent templets are laid. (a) Templets 1, 2, and 3 shown separately. In this illustration, only one photograph control point on each side of the center is used. (b) The first templet is placed to fit the three control points. (c) The second templet is placed on the first to fit control point B and to make 1—2' coincide with 2—1'. Note the new points p thus located opposite the center of 2. (d) The third templet is placed to fit the new points p and to make 2—3' coincide with 3—2'. The new points q are now located opposite the center of 3, and are used to place templet 4, and so on to the next ground control.

points will also be on templet 3 and will thus provide a means of locating the latter templet, even if it has no ground control. Templet 3 is moved over No. 2, keeping lines 2—3' and 3—2' coincident until the rays on No. 3 pass through these points. The remaining templets of the flight are located in a similar way, the procedure being repeated until another line of ground control is reached. Any discrepancy or "error of closure" on these control points is then adjusted back through the flight. When subsequent flights are laid, they must be made to fit not only the ground control points but also the photographic control points common to the flights already laid. When the photographs are marked, care should be taken to see that there are several of these common points. In making this adjustment, it will be necessary to disrupt the perfect coincidences of center lines and the point intersections that were maintained in the original lay-down. It is best to keep this disruption as small as possible, usually by distributing the error of closure over the whole flight, throwing each templet out by a small amount so that the discrepancy at any one point or on any one center line may be scarcely noticeable.

6–10. Base Sheets. The result of this adjusted layout is the location of each photograph center upon the base sheet together with a considerable

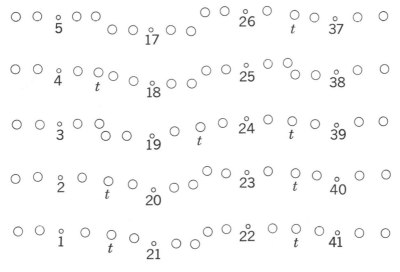

Fig. 6–3. Portion of a base map showing located photograph centers and radial control points. Here two points on each side of the centers were located, those marked *t* being common to two flights.

number, theoretically unlimited, of photographic control points distributed throughout the area (Fig. 6–3). It would be possible to mark these on the base sheet by pricking through the templets, but this would involve the penetration of at least three and sometimes as many as six thicknesses of acetate, which not only would constitute a considerable task but might introduce excessive error in marking the points. Probably a better way is to lay a sheet of transparent material over the layout and mark the points on this from the top. An alternative is to use such a piece for the base sheet itself, in which case the entire layout, after the templets have been securely fastened, can be turned over and the points marked from the bottom.

6–11. Slotted Templets. A slotted templet* is made of rather stiff pasteboard in which narrow slots radiating from the center correspond to the various points marked on the photograph, including the conjugate

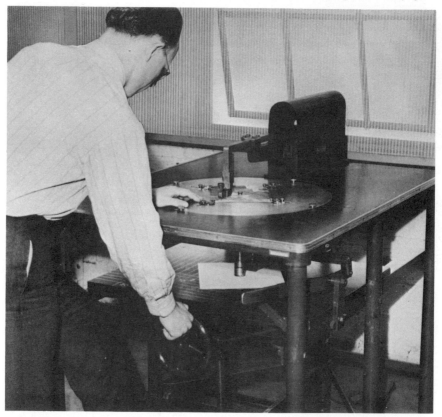

FIG. 6–4. Machine for cutting slots in templets. (Photography by Commodity Stabilization Service, U. S. Department of Agriculture.)

centers. The cutting is done by a special machine (Fig. 6–4) in which the photograph and the templet blank are mounted in parallel planes, the two mounts being connected to turn as a unit. By rotating the mounts until a point is aligned with an index mark, the templet is brought into correct

* Developed by C. W. Collier in 1936.

relation with the cutter blade. When completed, the templets are assembled with small rivet-like studs whose diameters just fit the slots in the templets (Fig. 6–5). The centers of the studs, which are hollow for marking purposes, then represent the locations of the points. Fig. 6–6 shows an assembly of these templets covering more than twenty flight strips.

6–12. Mechanical Templets. The mechanical templet* is similar to the slotted templet in that the directions to the points are represented by narrow

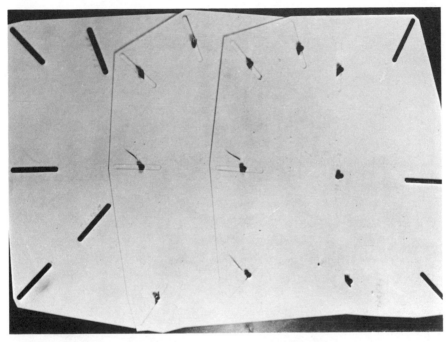

Fig. 6–5. How slotted templets fit together. (Photography by Commodity Stabilization Service, U. S. Department of Agriculture.)

slots, but here they are in thin, slender, metal arms. These arms are assembled in the correct positions by pins placed through the center of the photograph and through each point, upon which a bushing and stud are placed. The arms are then fitted over the center bushing, the slot of each being also fitted over the stud of a point. After all arms are in place, they are held securely by a nut tightened over the center bushing. The templets are then assembled in a manner similar to that for the slotted templets previously described. Such an assembly is pictured in Fig. 6–7 and a kit for constructing the templets is shown in Fig. 6–8.

An advantage of these latter two types of templets is that several strips may be assembled and fitted to the control points at the same time, the

* Developed by S. P. Floore in 1938.

adjustments being made largely by slight bucklings within the templets themselves. In the transparent type, each templet must be adjusted individually. This may become a rather painstaking task.

Transfer of Planimetry

6–13. Photographic Control Points. The radial control plot provides a base map with the locations of a number of photographic control points.

Fig. 6–6. Slotted templets assembled for several flights. The black triangles represent ground control points. (Photography by Commodity Stabilization Service, U.S. Department of Agriculture.)

Unlike the usual run of ground control, which is necessarily confined to limited areas or lines, these photographic control points are well distributed throughout the area, several points being located opposite each photograph center by the very nature of the process itself. Furthermore, an unlimited number of additional points may be located as desired, being simply "cut in" by intersections of rays from two or more photograph centers.

6–14. Details. Included among these control points may be a few of the objects which are to be shown on the finished map, but there will certainly be many which are not. With a few exceptions, any detail point could be located by an intersection from photograph centers, but this would develop into a rather tiresome task if many such points were involved. Faster methods of transferring details from the photographs to the base map include direct tracing, and plotting with such instruments as the vertical sketchmaster, projector, and radial plotter.

6–15. Direct Tracing. About the simplest and least expensive method is to trace the details directly from the photographs themselves. This can readily be done if the base map has been plotted to a scale that is nearly the

Fig. 6–7. An assembly of mechanical templets. (Photo from files of Gordon Enterprises.)

same as the "average" scale of the photography. Because of relief displacements, an exact fitting of photographs to the base plot is rarely possible.

A tracing of the base map is placed over one of the photographs and adjusted until two *adjacent* control points on the photograph are brought into coincidence as nearly as possible to the corresponding map points. The required details (roads, streams, houses, etc.) are then traced in the area between these two points. Generally, the photograph and base map points will not match exactly, and an adjustment becomes necessary as the tracing proceeds from one point to the next. This may be done by sliding the tracing over the photograph a little at a time until the second point is reached.

6–16. Errors. The accuracy of this method depends largely upon the regularity of the ground surface between control points. Two points could match perfectly, and yet the intermediate plotting would be considerably in error if there are marked changes in elevation between them. This error can be lessened by locating more points on the radial control plot, thus reducing

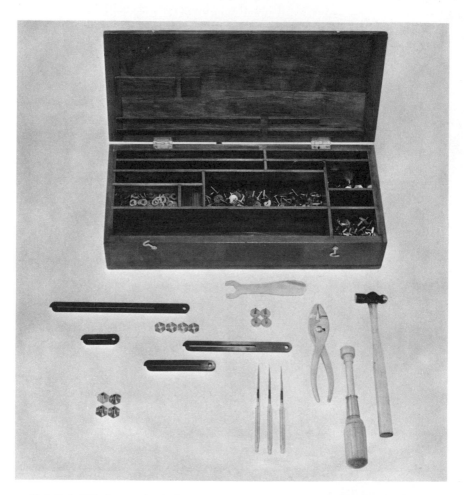

Fig. 6–8. Kit for mechanical templet construction. (Photo from files of Gordon Enterprises.)

the distances between them. Furthermore, it is preferable to confine the tracing as much as possible to the central portion of each picture, unless another choice gives better conformity to the scale of the map.

6–17. Vertical Sketchmaster. The vertical sketchmaster (Fig. 6–9) is a device by which the base plot and the photograph are viewed simultaneously.

It is much the same in principle as direct tracing in that details are drawn between points after they have been brought into apparent coincidence on photograph and map. Much more latitude as to relative scale is possible with this instrument, since the height above the table can be varied by changing the length of the supporting legs.

Fig. 6–9. Vertical sketchmaster. (Photo from files of Gordon Enterprises.)

As shown in Fig. 6–10, the photograph is reflected first by mirror M_1 and then by the small mirror M_2 to the observer's eye at E. At the same time, the map is seen directly, and the two may be so placed that the point A on the map and its corresponding image a on the photograph will appear to coincide. With the legs at the proper height, a second point B may be made to coincide with b, and by tipping the instrument, thus tilting the plane of the photograph, it is possible to make three points coincide. This tilting does not usually represent the actual tilt of the photograph, since the points may be displaced as a result of relief. It simply allows the details over a larger part of the photograph to be traced with one setting of the instrument.

Like direct tracing, plotting with the sketchmaster is affected by the error resulting from relief displacements between control points, so that coincidence of the latter does not necessarily mean accurate detail location. Its advantage lies in the ability to fit the photograph better in scale and to provide coincidence of adjacent points, thus reducing the adjustment to a minimum as the tracing proceeds.

6–18. Reflecting Projector. In a projector (Fig. 6–11), the photograph placed in a holder at the top of the instrument is reflected to the base map on the table. Thus, as in the sketchmaster, the points on the map and the corresponding points of the photograph can be made to coincide. The details as projected may then be traced on the map, using pairs of adjacent points as before. Usually a considerable range of adjustment is available so that the points can be brought into coincidence quite readily. If, in addition, the table upon which the photograph is projected can also be tilted, three points can be brought into coincidence and the details traced within that triangle.

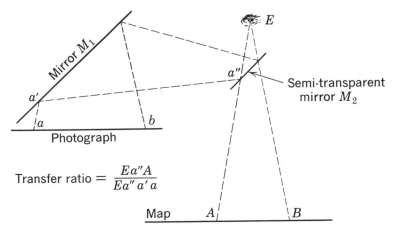

$$\text{Transfer ratio} = \frac{Ea''A}{Ea''a'a}$$

FIG. 6–10. Schematic diagram of sketchmaster.

With a photograph placed in the holder (Fig. 6–12), a light source S illuminates the photograph, rays from which are reflected by the mirror through the lens L and thence to the table. The photograph, lens, and table must be in a relative position such that $1/I + 1/O = 1/f$, where f is the focal length of the lens. I/O is then the ratio of enlargement.

6–19. Second Method. It may be noted that the photograph can be brought into its correct scale at each point by always keeping the center of the photograph at its map location and by simply changing the ratio of projection so that each point in turn is brought into coincidence. If the details around each point were all at approximately the same elevation as the point itself, they would then be in their theoretically correct location. Since this is seldom true, at least in hilly or mountainous terrain, little may be gained from using this procedure.

6–20. Radial Plotter. In the radial plotter (Fig. 6–13), two overlapping photographs are viewed stereoscopically, the details in their common area being transferred to the map through a mechanical linkage. The photographs are fastened on small platforms and oriented for exact stereoscopic viewing,

Fig. 6–11. Reflecting projector. (Courtesy of Reed Research, Inc.)

as outlined in Art. 3–18. Radial arms of transparent material held by pins through the centers of the photographs can be rotated to any portion of the overlapping area. When viewed under the stereoscope, fine lines etched

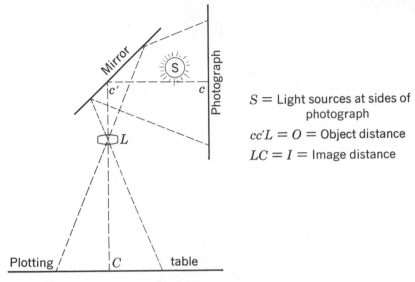

S = Light sources at sides of photograph

$cc'L = O$ = Object distance

$LC = I$ = Image distance

FIG. 6–12. Schematic diagram of reflecting projector.

FIG. 6–13. Radial planimetric plotter. (Courtesy of Philip B. Kail Associates.)

along the centers of these arms will appear to form a floating cross, which can be set on any point in the overlapping area of the two photographs.

Through the mechanical linkage (Fig. 6–14), which is provided with an adjustment for scale, a tracing pencil assumes the corresponding map position of this same point.

6–21. Orientation. The principal points plotted on the radial control sheet can be used to orient the instrument. The floating mark is considered to be set on the left principal point when the right arm is along the flight

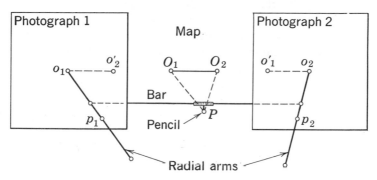

FIG. 6–14. Schematic diagram of radial plotter. The connecting bar is maintained in position by a parallel-motion device not shown.

line and the left arm is perpendicular to it (Fig. 6–15). Lines are etched on the photograph platforms to indicate these positions. With the cross thus set on one principal point, the plotter is moved bodily until the tracing pencil rests on the corresponding map point and the flight lines of photographs and map are parallel by estimation. The cross is then set on the other

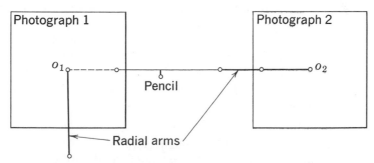

FIG. 6–15. Radial arms set on principal point of photograph 1.

principal point and, if the orientation were correct, the pencil would now rest on the map position of this point. A failure to agree in direction can be corrected by rotating the instrument as nearly as possible about the first principal point as a center, while a discrepancy in distance is corrected by the scale adjustment screw on the linkage bar. This process is repeated until all points are in substantial coincidence throughout the overlap.

6–22. Plotting. Any item of detail can then be plotted by placing the floating cross on the desired point and marking the map with the tracing pencil. A road, or other line detail, can be traced on the map by manipulating the radial arms so that the cross appears to follow the road, the tracing pencil at the same time plotting its location on the map.

6–23. Comparison of Methods. It may be pointed out that, of the instruments or methods described, this is the only type that provides location of details theoretically free from errors resulting from relief displacements. In effect, every point is located by radial-line intersections from the centers of two photographs, thus eliminating the effects of relief. Methods of transferring from a single photograph, whether by direct tracing, sketchmaster, or a projector, suffer from the inevitable relief displacements of images between control points. If the elevation variation is slight, or if it is at a uniform rate between control points, the effect is small; but with large or irregular differences in elevation, considerable error in position may result. One way of reducing this effect is to locate additional points by radial-line intersections on the radial control network, thus reducing the distances between adjacent points and also providing for the selection of points at locations which give more uniform slopes.

Contouring by Nonstereoscopic Methods

6–24. Topographic Mapping. The radial-line control network and subsequent transfer of details produce a planimetric map. A topographic map further requires the delineation of contours. Probably the most satisfactory solution for the photogrammetrist is to utilize the photographs themselves for determining and plotting the location of these contours. The stereoscopic procedures and some of the instruments which have been devised and constructed for this purpose are discussed in subsequent chapters (see Chapters 7 and 11). However, there are some combinations of photographic and standard ground mapping methods which can be used to produce a satisfactory topographic map.

6–25. Contour Plotting. With the planimetric map completed, elevations of key points can be determined by ground survey methods, plotted on the map, and contours located by the usual method of interpolation. The elevations might be determined by barometric levels, trigonometric leveling, direct leveling, or a combination of these, generally depending upon the accuracy required. The key points should be those marking important changes in slope of the ground, and with judicious selection, the contours can be plotted with a surprisingly small total number of these elevations. In so far as the topographic work is concerned in this method, photogrammetry plays only an incidental role. For example, the photographs might aid the field level crews in planning their routes and selection of elevation points to the best advantage. Also the photographs, viewed stereoscopically, could greatly help the contourer in the interpretation of the terrain, dependence being placed on the field elevation mainly for the quantitative values of the contours.

6–26. Stereoscopic Devices. In a second method, the elevations are determined from the photographs with stereoscopic devices, the actual contouring again being by interpolation between adjacent points of known elevation. The principles and instruments used for determining these spot elevations are discussed in Chapter 7.

An advantage of this method over the preceding is that more points can be determined, very likely with a better distribution throughout the area, since rough terrain is no deterrent. It should be noted that the contours themselves are not obtained by photogrammetric methods, but rather the elevations from which they are subsequently plotted.

6–27. Plane Table. The planimetric map may be mounted on a plane table and the contours drawn, using regular plane-table methods with alidade and stadia for the determination of elevations of key controlling points. The contours can then be sketched, an advantage being that the topographer is on the ground and can observe directly the pattern of the terrain. The completed map would thus consist of planimetric details by photogrammetric methods and contours by plane-table methods. While in the field for the latter operation, the plane tabler may also check the photogrammetric interpretation of the cultural and natural details.

Instead of the map, which perhaps is not yet available, the photographs themselves, usually enlarged to some convenient approximate scale, may be used on the plane table (Figs. 6–16, 6–17). Directions cannot be expected to check closely, but the photograph can be oriented and elevations of points can be spotted with sufficient accuracy for plotting contours directly on the photograph. Again, being on the ground makes it easier for the topographer to delineate the contours. After they have been drawn on the photograph, these contours can then be transferred to the map in the office, just as cultural and natural details are transferred from photographs to map as described in Arts. 6–15 through 6–22.

6–28. Choice of Method. Whether some one or more of these methods should be considered, instead of the all-photogrammetric methods treated later, may depend upon the equipment and personnel available. In many instances it may be that a satisfactory topographic map can be produced by one of these less expensive methods where the investment in additional photogrammetric equipment does not seem economically advisable.

LABORATORY PROBLEMS

Lab. Prob. 6–1. Establish a radial-line control network for a flight strip of five or more photographs. Use cellulose acetate, tracing cloth, or tracing paper for the templets. Actual ground control is desirable, but points may be picked from good existing maps as a substitute. If this is done, it may be best to lay the templets at a random scale which will later be determined by comparing one or more distances between points at opposite ends of the strip. If it is then desired to change the plot to some specific scale, the templets can be shifted according to the ratio of actual to desired scales. For convenience in later

FIG. 6–16. Plotting contours on aerial photograph by plane-table methods. (Courtesy of U. S. Coast and Geodetic Survey.)

mapping procedures, it may be desirable to have the map scale approximately the same as that of the photographs. The resulting product consists of a base sheet showing each photograph center with its number, ground control points, and photograph control points. These should be marked with circles of the same size and color as those used in marking the photographs themselves. Letter a suitable title and north arrow.

If time and photographs are available, this problem may be extended to include two or more flight strips, care being taken to select several common points for tying the flights together.

Lab. Prob. 6–2. Plot the planimetric details on the radial-line control base map constructed in Lab. Prob. 6–1. Use methods according to the equipment available,

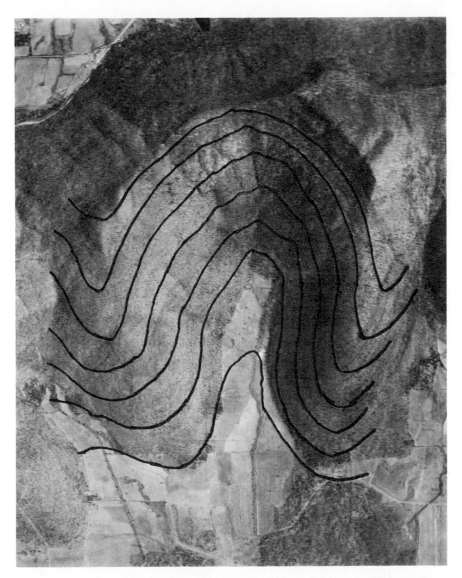

FIG. 6–17. Portion of aerial photograph with contours added. (Courtesy of U. S. Coast and Geodetic Survey.)

making as many duplicate tracings of the base map as needed. Plot the roads, railroads, major drainage features, transmission lines, and any other principal objects that occur on the particular photographs used. Individual buildings are to be shown if time permits. Label names of communities, railroads, drainage features, and highway route numbers. Letter a suitable title on each plot and show a north arrow.

7

STEREOSCOPIC PRINCIPLES

7–1. Importance of the Stereoscope. The use of the stereoscope for three-dimensional viewing was described in Chapter 3. The importance of this instrument in aerial photographic work can hardly be overstressed, and the principles of stereoscopy now to be considered will emphasize even more its value in connection with measuring and plotting equipment. Indeed, these principles are fundamental to the understanding of any stereoscopic instrument for plotting from aerial photographs, whether simple or complex.

7–2. Binocular Vision. A person with reasonably normal vision in both eyes is provided with a sense of relative distance. That is, within certain limits, he can tell which of two objects is closer to him, even if their spatial relationship is not evident through any other means. This is because the eyes, being some $2\frac{1}{2}$ inches apart, regard objects at slightly different angles, a

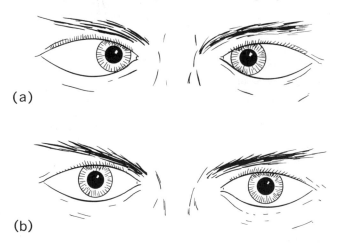

(a)

(b)

Fig. 7–1. Convergence of the eyes for different distances: (a) looking at a near object; (b) looking at a far object.

situation which is analogous to the location of details by turning angles at the ends of a base line. When looking at a close object, the eyes converge quite sharply; they become more nearly parallel as the object recedes (Fig. 7–1). The convergence is communicated to the brain, which interprets it as a measure of distance. As the distance increases, the convergence gets smaller until at some point it becomes so slight that it is no longer sensible to the brain. Beyond this, any conception of distance must be gained through other means, for example, by the relative apparent sizes of known objects.

7–3. Stereoscopic Viewing. Considering the eyes as they regard two objects A and B at different distances (Fig. 7–2), suppose a transparent sheet is placed in front of them and marks are made on it at points which appear to be in line with A and B. Now, if the sheet is viewed so that the

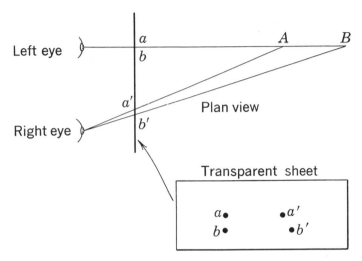

Fig. 7–2. How the eyes give the sense of distance. (A and B are here taken as points in a vertical plane with the left eye.)

left eye sees only the left dots and the right eye only the right dots, it will be discovered that with some practice and perseverance, the corresponding dots will fuse. It will then appear as though the eyes are looking directly at the points A and B in space rather than at the separate images, and A and B will appear to be at their respective distances, thus reproducing the third dimension of actual space.

7–4. Photographs. Consider now that the eyes are replaced by camera lenses and the transparent sheet by photographs, which would duplicate the situation of vertical aerial photography. With the customary 60 per cent overlap between adjacent photographs, this common area is seen from two different points. By orienting the two photographs for stereoscopic viewing, the third dimension will become sensible, as though each eye were at one of the camera stations in space.

7–5. Parallax. It will now be seen that two adjacent photographs may be used to determine the elevations of ground points whose images appear upon them (Fig. 7–3). The flying height above the datum is H, the distance between photograph stations L_1 and L_2 is B, the focal length of the camera is f, and the elevation of a ground point Q is h. The difference in the direction of Q as seen from the two stations is called its *parallax*. Strictly speaking, parallax is an angle which, for the point Q, would be represented by α. If a line is constructed at L_1 parallel to L_2Q, the angle $q''L_1q$ is then equal to the parallax angle. Parallax is important in photogrammetric processes, but it

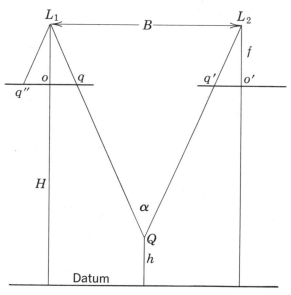

Fig. 7–3. Theory of parallax.

is more convenient to use linear quantities, which are readily scaled from the photographs, than the angular value just defined. Therefore, instead of the angle α, the linear intercept $q''oq$ will be used, this in turn being equal to $oq + o'q'$. If the line of flight L_1L_2 is taken as the x-axis of coordinates on the photographs, then the parallax (according to this revised definition) is the difference in the two x-coordinates. It should be noted that $o'q'$ in the above addition is actually a negative quantity, since q' is to the left of o'.

7–6. Elevations from Parallax. In Fig. 7–3, since the triangles L_1L_2Q and $q''L_1q$ are similar, the following relations may be written:

$$f/q''q = f/p = (H - h)/B \qquad (7\text{–}1)$$

where p equals the linear parallax for the point Q. Then

$$H - h = Bf/p \qquad \text{or} \qquad h = H - Bf/p \qquad (7\text{–}2)$$

Thus, with the flying height, the distance between photograph exposure stations, and the camera focal length known, this provides a method for determining elevations of ground points which are identifiable on the photographs.

The above relationship will prove helpful later when it will be used in the determination of elevations and for contouring with some of the simpler types of plotting instruments; at present, however, it will be shown how spot elevations can be obtained from a pair of photographs with only an engineer's scale. The methods shown here may be modified in later work.

7–7. Parallax Measurements. For measuring parallax, the two photographs are oriented so that the lines of centers coincide and images are the proper distance apart for good stereoscopic vision (Fig. 7–4). It is important

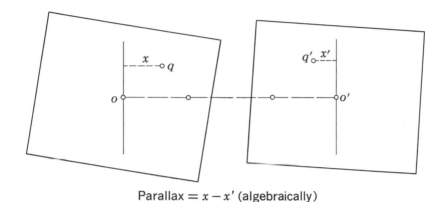

Parallax $= x - x'$ (algebraically)

FIG. 7–4. Measurement of parallax on two overlapping photographs.

that this orientation be made very carefully. Through the center of each photograph a line is then drawn perpendicular to the line of centers, these being the y-axes of the photographs for this particular pair. The x-coordinates are measured with a finely graduated engineer's scale, and the parallaxes are determined from their algebraic differences. Elevations of the points can then be calculated.

EXAMPLE 7–1. For two successive vertical photographs, the flying height is 10,000 ft., the distance between photograph stations is 5,000 ft., and the camera focal length is $8\frac{1}{4}$ in. The following coordinates to a point are measured parallel to the line of flight from axes through the centers: on the left photograph, $+3.08$ in., on the right photograph, -1.83 in. Determine the elevation of the point.

$$p = +3.08 - (-1.83) = 4.91 \text{ in.}$$

$$h = H - \frac{Bf}{p} = 10,000 - \frac{5000 \times 8.25}{4.91} = 10,000 - 8400 = 1600 \text{ ft.}$$

7–8. Determination of B and H. The values of B and H, if not known, can be determined, provided two or more ground points, identifiable on the photographs and at considerably different heights, are known in elevation.

Measuring the parallax for each, two simultaneous equations in H and B can be written from Eq. 7–2. Solving,

$$h_2 - h_1 = Bf(1/p_1 - 1/p_2)$$

or

$$B = \frac{h_2 - h_1}{f(1/p_1 - 1/p_2)} \qquad (7\text{–}3)$$

It is thus seen that the difference in h's should be fairly large, or the solution would approach the indeterminate form $0/0$. Also,

$$\frac{H - h_1}{H - h_2} = \frac{p_2}{p_1} \qquad \text{and} \qquad p_1(H - h_1) = p_2(H - h_2)$$

$$p_1 H - p_2 H = p_1 h_1 - p_2 h_2$$

So

$$H = \frac{p_1 h_1 - p_2 h_2}{p_1 - p_2} \qquad (7\text{–}4)$$

EXAMPLE 7–2. Values of B and H are to be determined for two successive aerial photographs, the focal length being 6 in. The following information is known for two ground points appearing in the overlap:

Point	Elevation	x-Coordinate	
		Left Photograph	Right Photograph
1	250 ft.	+2.46 in.	−1.07 in.
2	820 ft.	+4.11 in.	+0.16 in.

$$p_1 = +2.46 - (-1.07) = 3.53 \text{ in.}$$
$$p_2 = +4.11 - (+0.16) = 3.95 \text{ in.}$$

$$B = \frac{h_2 - h_1}{f\left(\dfrac{1}{p_1} - \dfrac{1}{p_2}\right)} = \frac{820 - 250}{6\left(\dfrac{1}{3.53} - \dfrac{1}{3.95}\right)} = \frac{570}{6(0.283 - 0.253)} = \frac{570}{6 \times 0.030} = 3165 \text{ ft.}$$

$$H = \frac{p_1 h_1 - p_2 h_2}{p_1 - p_2} = \frac{(3.53 \times 250) - (3.95 \times 820)}{3.53 \times 3.95} = \frac{882 - 3240}{-0.42} = \frac{2358}{0.42} = 5620 \text{ ft.}$$

Elementary Stereoscopic Devices

7–9. Principal Parts. The theories underlying stereoscopic viewing and the measurement of parallax can be applied to aerial photographs with rather simple and relatively inexpensive equipment. Indeed, as was observed in Art. 7–7, it is possible to determine elevations with little more than an engineer's scale. The simple instruments described here can all be used for determining elevations, and some are adapted for plotting contours. They consist essentially of five components: (1) a stereoscope, (2) a floating mark, (3) a parallax measuring scale, (4) a parallel motion device, and (5) a tracing arm and pencil. The last two items are not necessary for determining elevations only.

7–10. Stereoscopes. The stereoscope is usually a simple one, in some cases only a folding pocket model (Fig. 7–5), while in others it may be more

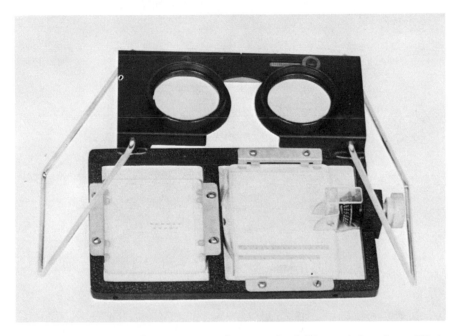

Fig. 7–5. The Austin Interpretometer for measuring heights and elevations. (Photo from files of Gordon Enterprises.)

elaborate, possibly of the mirror type (Fig. 7–6). The latter gives an advantage in wider spacing of the photographs and consequently less interference in viewing. Not only is the stereoscope an invaluable aid in viewing aerial photographs for any purpose, but it is indispensable for contouring and a great help in determining spot elevations.

7–11. Floating Marks. The floating mark is commonly provided by two glass crystals, one directly under each lens or mirror of the stereoscope, hinged to the frame of the instrument so that it may either lie flat on the photograph or be raised out of view. On each glass there is etched a distinctive mark, such as a dot or cross, which can be fused stereoscopically, just as are images on the two photographs. Furthermore, one of the glasses can be moved laterally with respect to the other. This gives the fused mark an appearance of rising or lowering in elevation when viewed through the stereoscope. With this adjustment, the fused image of the floating mark can be made to rest directly upon some fused image of the photographs.

7–12. Parallax Scale. The relative movement of the two parts of the floating mark can be controlled by a micrometer screw, which gives a scale reading for any setting of the mark. While the reading can theoretically be

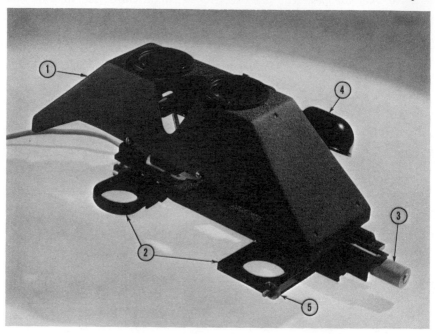

FIG. 7–6. Stereocomparagraph. (1) Stereoscope, (2) floating-mark lenses, (3) microm-eter screw, (4) lamp, (5) *y*-parallax adjustment. Chucks for attaching drafting machine and tracing arm are at rear of base (see Fig. 7–8). The stereocomparagraph was invented by Capt. Benjamin B. Talley in 1935. (Courtesy of Fairchild Camera & Instrument Corporation.)

made equal to the parallax, this is not necessary and in practice is not usually done, since in most cases only differences in parallax are needed. These can be obtained by the subtraction of readings, so that their absolute values are of little importance. The reading for any point can be considered as its absolute parallax plus some undetermined constant; when one reading is subtracted from another, the constant is eliminated.

The floating mark and scale are perhaps the most important parts of these instruments. Certainly the mark is helpful in setting on points, and it is absolutely essential for contouring. The scale is necessary if numerical values of elevations and contours are desired, but it need not be used if only form lines* are to be plotted.

* Form lines show the *shape* of the ground's surface, as do contours, but without denoting specific elevations.

7–13. Parallel Motion. It is convenient in measuring spot elevations and necessary in contouring that the axis of the instrument maintain the direction of its original orientation as it is moved over the photographs. An ordinary drafting machine or some similar type of parallel-motion device may be fastened to the frame of the instrument. That the parallel motion need not be as accurate as the orientation of the photographs on their centers is readily apparent. For a point well out from the line of centers, a relatively small rotation of one of the photographs from its true position will directly introduce an error of considerable amount in the parallax measurement of the point. A corresponding rotation of the instrument, on the other hand, will have only a negligible effect upon the parallax measurement.

7–14. Tracing Point. A tracing point is not needed for spot elevations, but it is essential for drawing contours and for any plotting of cultural and natural details. The tracer consists of an arm fastened to a part of the frame and extending to the rear, perhaps 10 or 12 inches. A tracing pencil is held at the end of the arm, and either it alone or the entire arm can be moved vertically so that the point can be raised from the paper or lowered to drawing position as the operator may wish.

The point will then trace a line parallel to the path of the fixed component of the floating mark, usually the left, no provision being made for a change of scale. A contour is thus drawn to the scale of the left photograph for that particular elevation. Each contour therefore is at a different scale.

7–15. Elevations. Assume that two photographs have been correctly set for the instrument, that in the overlapping area there is at least one identifiable point whose elevation is known, and that the elevations of several other points are to be determined. While looking through the stereoscope, the operator moves the instrument rapidly over the photographs until the floating mark appears to rest nearly upon the control point; he then brings the mark and point into exact coincidence by whatever final movement of the instrument and adjustment of the micrometer screw may be necessary. Since the latter causes the floating mark to rise or fall in elevation, it may appear considerably above the ground for one setting while at another it may go below the surface (Fig. 7–7). In the latter case, the two component marks usually split and no longer give a fused image. Perhaps this is because the mind more readily comprehends an object floating above the ground than below it. The micrometer is read when the mark appears to rest directly upon the point. In like manner, the instrument is moved and set in turn on each of the various points whose elevations are desired, and the micrometer is read for each setting.

From Equation (7–1),

$$\frac{f}{p} = \frac{H - h}{B} \qquad \text{or} \qquad p = \frac{Bf}{H - h}$$

Letting the elevations of two points 1 and 2 be represented by h_1 and h_2 and the corresponding parallaxes by p_1 and p_2,

$$p_1 = \frac{Bf}{H - h_1} \qquad \text{and} \qquad p_2 = \frac{Bf}{H - h_2}$$

By subtraction,

$$p_1 - p_2 = \frac{Bf}{H - h_1} - \frac{Bf}{H - h_2} = \frac{Bf(h_2 - h_1)}{(H - h_1)(H - h_2)}$$

or

$$\Delta p = \frac{Bf\,\Delta h}{(H - h_1)(H - h_2)} \qquad\qquad (7\text{--}5)$$

and

$$\Delta h = \frac{(H - h_1)(H - h_2)}{Bf}\,\Delta p \qquad\qquad (7\text{--}6)$$

The micrometer reading for each new point subtracted from that for the control point gives the difference in parallax between them, or the Δp of

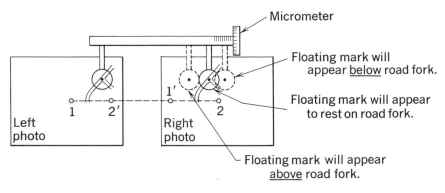

FIG. 7–7. Setting the floating mark. Note also the orientation of the photographs: centers 1 and 2 and transferred centers 1' and 2' are all on the same line.

Eq. 7–6.* The value of Δh is then calculated, which, when added to the base point's elevation, yields the elevation of the new point. It is again emphasized that the micrometer reading in itself represents no particular quantity, although it differs from the absolute parallax by some undetermined number. However, the difference between two readings is a true difference in parallax.

The solution of Eq. 7–6 involves one of the unknown elevations. If

* It must be determined for the particular instrument being used whether the parallax reading increases or decreases with elevation; this can be done by noting that the elevation increases as the two components of the floating mark are brought together.

Δh is small, little error will be introduced by assuming that $h_1 = h_2 = h$, and the expression then becomes

$$\Delta h = \frac{(H - h)^2 \, \Delta p}{Bf} \qquad (7\text{--}7)$$

When Δh is large, the value obtained by Eq. 7–7 is subject to a correction, which may be determined as follows:

In Eq. 7–6, replace h_2 by $h_1 + \Delta h$, and let the trial value be denoted by $\Delta h'$.

Then

$$\Delta h = \frac{(H - h_1)(H - h_1 - \Delta h) \, \Delta p}{Bf}$$

$$= \frac{(H - h_1)^2 \, \Delta p}{Bf} - \frac{\Delta h(H - h_1) \, \Delta p}{Bf}$$

$$= \Delta h' - \frac{\Delta h}{(H - h_1)} \Delta h'$$

The second term in this expression is thus the correction which may be written:

$$\text{Correction} = -\frac{\Delta h'}{(H - h_1)} \Delta h \qquad (7\text{--}8)$$

where Δh is taken as the best available value at any stage of the calculation, which at the start would be $\Delta h'$ itself, and except for extreme differences in elevation will be sufficiently close. However, a second or even third calculation may be made if necessary, using the newest value of Δh each time.

EXAMPLE 7–3. For two successive vertical photographs, $H = 10,000$ ft., $B = 3000$ ft., and $f = 210$ mm. The following micrometer readings are taken on points in the overlapping area, the readings increasing with elevation. Calculate the elevations of the new points.

Point	Elevation	Micrometer Reading
BM	850 ft.	15.48 mm.
1	To be determined	16.03 mm.
2	To be determined	13.22 mm.

Point 1: $\Delta p = 16.03 - 15.48 = +0.55$ mm.

$$\Delta h' = \frac{(H - h)^2 \, \Delta p}{Bf} = \frac{(9150)^2 \times 0.55}{3000 \times 210} = +73 \text{ ft.}$$

$$\text{Correction} = -\frac{\Delta h'}{(H - h)} \Delta h = -\frac{73.0 \times 73.0}{9150} = -0.6 \text{ ft. (negligible)}$$

Elevation of $1 = 850 + 73 = 923$ ft.

Point 2: $\Delta p = 13.22 - 15.48 = -2.26$ mm.

$$\Delta h' = \frac{(9150)^2 \times 2.26}{3000 \times 210} = -300 \text{ ft.}$$

$$\text{Correction} = -\frac{300 \times 300}{9150} = -9.8, \text{ say } 10 \text{ ft.}$$

$$\Delta h = -300 - 10 = -310 \text{ ft.}$$

Apply the correction equation a second time, using this value of Δh.

$$\text{Correction} = -\frac{300 \times 310}{9150} = -10.2 \text{ ft., or practically no change}$$

Elevation of 2 = 850 − 310 = 540 ft.

7–16. Tilt. It has been assumed that the photographs were truly vertical with absolutely no tilt. As noted previously, this is an impossible condition to obtain, and undoubtedly both photographs will have some, though perhaps not large, amounts of tilt. Tilts, unless exceedingly small, will cause displacements of images which will introduce errors in the parallax readings and consequently errors in the calculated elevations, sometimes of considerable magnitude. A method of correcting for this situation is discussed in Chapter 10.

7–17. y-Parallax. As the instrument is moved over the photographs, it may be found that the floating mark fails to rest on the ground, not only because of image displacements parallel to the line of flight, but also by displacements perpendicular to it. This latter is called y-parallax and may be caused by tilt and small differences in flying height between the two photographs. One of the glass holders is commonly provided with a small movement in the y direction to allow an adjustment for this situation. This is illustrated by the small screw (5) in Fig. 7–6.

7–18. Contours. For contouring, the difference between the elevation of the desired contour and a base point gives a "Δh," which may be inserted in Eq. 7–6, yielding a "Δp." This, applied to the micrometer reading on the base point, gives the setting to be made for the particular contour. Usually there is a provision for locking this setting in order to prevent any accidental movement of the micrometer screw. There is no approximation in this solution, since both elevations are known at the start of the computation.

EXAMPLE 7–4. For the photographs of Example 7–3, calculate the micrometer setting for the 1000-ft. contour.

$$\Delta h = 1000 - 850 = 150 \text{ ft.}$$

$$\Delta p = \frac{Bf \times \Delta h}{(H - h_1)(H - h_2)} = \frac{3000 \times 210 \times 150}{(9150)(9000)} = +1.15 \text{ mm.}$$

New setting = 15.48 + 1.15 = 16.63 mm.

The operator now moves the instrument over the photographs somewhat at random until the fused floating mark appears to rest directly upon the ground, thus locating a point on the desired contour. That portion of the contour within the common area of the photographs is then traced by moving the instrument so that the mark is kept always in apparent contact with the ground (Fig. 7–8). It may be appreciated that this operation requires a

FIG. 7–8. Stereocomparagraph in use, with drafting machine and tracing arm. The pencil can be raised and lowered as desired. (Courtesy of Fairchild Camera & Instrument Corporation.)

considerable degree of skill obtained only through many hours of practice and that progress at first will be disappointingly slow, consisting of repeated trial and correction endeavors. The contours can be traced on a sheet of paper, each one being at the scale of the photograph for the particular elevation of that contour. After the photographic control and center points have also been plotted on this sheet, it can then be used to plot contours by tracing them directly to the map provided the scales of sheet and map are approximately the same. Also, the sheet may be used in a vertical sketchmaster or a reflecting projector, either of which allows for changing scale as required. These processes are similar to those for transferring details from the photograph as described in Chapter 6. In fact, the transfer sheet may be considered as the equivalent of the left photograph to the extent of the information plotted upon it.

PROBLEMS

7–1. $H = 10{,}500$ ft.; $B = 4500$ ft.; $f = 8\frac{1}{4}$ in. Calculate the elevations of the following points. Coordinates are parallel to the line of flight with respect to axes through the photograph centers.

Point	Coordinates	
	Left Photograph	Right Photograph
1	+2.55 in.	−1.38 in.
2	0.00 in.	−4.16 in.
3	+3.87 in.	+0.20 in.
4	−0.36 in.	−4.42 in.

7–2. $H = 7950$ ft.; $B = 2800$ ft.; $f = 150$ mm. Calculate the elevations of the following points. Coordinates are measured as in Prob. 7–1.

Point	Coordinates	
	Left Photograph	Right Photograph
1	+30.7 mm.	−25.5 mm.
2	+59.7 mm.	+ 1.3 mm.
3	− 5.4 mm.	−56.8 mm.
4	+40.7 mm.	−11.8 mm.

7–3. In Prob. 7–1, what would be the parallax for a point at datum?

7–4. In Prob. 7–2, what would be the parallax for a point at elevation 500 ft.? 1000 ft.? 5000 ft.?

7–5. In Prob. 7–1, the coordinate of a point on the left photograph is +2.48 in. The elevation of the point is 850 ft. What is the coordinate on the right photograph?

7–6. Calculate B and H from the following information on two ground points, the coordinates being measured as in the above problems. Focal length is 10 in.

Point	Elevation	Coordinates	
		Left Photograph	Right Photograph
1	2000 ft.	+4.09 in.	−0.87 in.
2	720 ft.	+2.74 in.	−1.46 in.

7–7. The flying height for two overlapping vertical photographs is 14,500 ft., the exposure stations are 4200 ft. apart, and the focal length is 210 mm. The following micrometer readings were taken on points within the area (readings increase with elevation). The elevation of G is 1220 ft; calculate the elevations of the other points.

Point	Micrometer Reading
G	8.28 mm.
H	8.53 mm.
J	7.97 mm.
K	11.74 mm.
L	6.02 mm.

7–8. Given: $H = 6000$ ft., $B = 2300$ ft., and $f = 150$ mm. Micrometer readings were made on points in the overlap as follows. Determine the elevations of the points, that of the bench mark being 275 ft.

Point	Micrometer Reading (increases with elevation)
BM	10.08 mm.
41	9.77 mm.
42	10.55 mm.
43	12.36 mm.
44	7.12 mm.

7–9. For Prob. 7–7, determine the micrometer setting for each 100-ft. contour from 800 to 1500, inclusive.

7–10. For Prob. 7–8, calculate the micrometer setting for each 50-ft. contour from 100 to 500, inclusive.

7–11. Calculate the absolute parallax for each point of Prob. 7–7. Does each differ from the corresponding reading by the same amount?

7–12. Calculate the absolute parallax for each point of Prob. 7–8.

LABORATORY PROBLEMS

Lab. Prob. 7–1. Orient two photographs for precise stereoscopic measurements. Using a stereoscope, select several points in the overlap whose elevations have been or can be determined by nonphotogrammetric methods. Mark the images of these points carefully on both photographs with a fine needle point. Establish the y-axis on each photograph perpendicular to the base line between centers. Then measure the parallax for each of the marked points with a finely divided scale.

Using the highest and lowest points, determine values for the base length (B) and the flying height (H) by Eqs. 7–3 and 7–4. Then determine the elevation of each of the remaining points by the parallax equation (Eq. 7–2). Compare results with the known elevations.

Lab. Prob. 7–2. Orient a pair of the photographs from the radial-line control problem of Chapter 6 for use with a stereocomparagraph or similar type of instrument. Fasten a blank sheet of paper to the table beneath the tracing arm. Set the floating mark in turn on each point that has been marked on the photographs (centers, radial-control points, and ground control points), and mark its location on the paper. These will give an exact duplicate of the left-hand photograph in so far as these points are concerned. Then plot or trace out the major planimetric features (roads, railroads, streams, buildings, etc.), keeping the floating mark in touch with the feature by adjusting the micrometer screw. When the details have been thus transferred to the paper plot, they may in turn be transferred from this to the base map by one of the methods outlined in Chapter 6, such as the sketchmaster or projector (not by the radial-line plotter, however).

Lab. Prob. 7–3. Orient two photographs as in the preceding problem. The elevations of several points in the overlap should be known (possibly from the Geological Survey quadrangle sheet or by barometric levels). Scale the length of B from the radial control plot; this will be the distance between the plotted locations of their centers. The value of H can be determined by measuring the parallax for one of the points known in elevation and solving by Eq. 7–2.

If the photographs used are not part of the radial plot, B and H can be determined by Eqs. 7–3 and 7–4 from two points of widely different elevation.

Read the micrometer scale for each of the selected points and calculate the values of Δp with respect to one of the points as a bench mark. Calculate the elevation of each point by Eq. 7–5 and compare with its known value.

Lab. Prob. 7–4. This is a continuation of Lab. Prob. 7–3, with paper fastened under the tracing arm as in Lab. Prob. 7–2. Using Eq. 7–6, calculate the micrometer reading for a given contour and set this on the scale. Move the instrument over the area of overlap until the floating mark appears to touch the ground surface. Lower the tracing pencil, thus plotting a point on the desired contour. Move the instrument so that the floating mark continues to touch the ground and the pencil will trace out the contour. When "exploring," be sure to raise the pencil from the paper to avoid making unnecessary and confusing marks. When one contour is completed, calculate the setting for the next and repeat the procedure. A suggested contour interval is approximately $\frac{1}{250} \times$ flying height.

8

TILT ANALYSIS

8–1. Image Displacements. It has previously been noted that even the small tilts of vertical photography cannot always be disregarded. Just as the displacement of an image resulting from elevation causes a change in photographic scale, as was shown in Art. 2–11, so also does any displacement resulting from tilt. An image displacement, whether caused by elevation or by tilt, may introduce an error if no correction is made for it.

Consider a photograph tilted through the angle t with respect to a horizontal photograph, as shown in Fig. 8–1. Points a and a' are the images

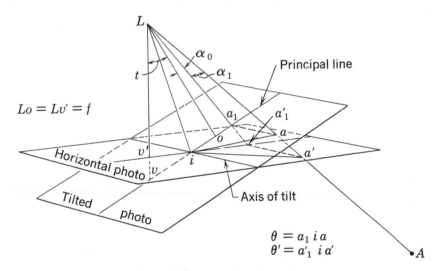

$$\theta = a_1\, i\, a$$
$$\theta' = a'_1\, i\, a'$$

FIG. 8–1. Relations in a tilted photograph.

of ground point A on the tilted and untilted photographs, respectively, while a_1 and a'_1 are the projections of these points onto the principal plane.*

8–2. Components of Displacement. If a is located on the photograph by coordinates x_a and y_a, with origin at o and ov as the negative y-axis, then

$$\tan \alpha_0 = y_a/f \tag{8–1}$$

and

$$\tan \alpha_1 = x_a/f \sec \alpha_0 \tag{8–2}$$

* The vertical plane which contains the principal point o and the nadir point v.

The displacement of the image resulting from tilt will be expressed by its components parallel and perpendicular to the principal line.* The parallel component, e_y, is equal to $ia'_1 - ia_1$.

$$ia'_1 = f \tan (t + \alpha_0) - f \tan t/2$$

and

$$ia_1 = f \tan \alpha_0 + f \tan t/2$$

So

$$e_y = f[\tan (t + \alpha_0) - \tan \alpha_0 - 2 \tan t/2] \qquad (8\text{--}3)$$

The perpendicular component, e_x, is equal to $a'_1a' - a_1a$.

$$a_1a = x_a = f \sec \alpha_0 \tan \alpha_1$$

and

$$a'_1a' = La'_1 \tan \alpha_1 = f \sec (t + \alpha_0) \tan \alpha_1$$

So

$$e_x = f \tan \alpha_1[\sec (t + \alpha_0) - \sec \alpha_0] \qquad (8\text{--}4)$$

Expressions 8–3 and 8–4 are of value mainly in analyzing the effects of assumed or known tilts upon images in various positions on the photograph and, in turn, the effects of these displacements upon elevations and directions.

EXAMPLE 8–1. The photograph coordinates of a point p with respect to the principal point as origin and the principal line as y-axis are: $x = +3.246$ in., $y = +2.307$ in. Focal length is 8.250 in. and the photograph is tilted 2° 20′. Calculate the image displacement resulting from tilt.

By Eq. 8–1, $\tan \alpha_0 = \dfrac{2.307}{8.250} = 0.27964 \qquad \alpha_0 = 15° \ 37′$

By Eq. 8–2, $\tan \alpha_1 = \dfrac{3.246}{8.250 \times 1.03834} = 0.37893 \qquad \alpha_1 = 20° \ 45′$

By Eq. 8–3, $e_y = f(\tan 17° \ 57′ - \tan 15° \ 37′ - 2 \tan 1° \ 10′)$

$$= 8.250 \ (0.32396 - 0.27952 - 0.04072) = 8.250 \times 0.00372$$

$$= 0.0307 \text{ in.}$$

By Eq. 8–4, $e_x = f \tan 20° \ 45′ (\sec 17° \ 57′ - \sec 15° \ 37′)$

$$= 8.250 \times 0.37887 \ (1.05116 - 1.03834)$$

$$= 8.250 \times 0.37887 \times 0.01282$$

$$= 0.0401 \text{ in.}$$

Total displacement $= \sqrt{(0.0307)^2 + (0.0401)^2} = 0.0505$ in.

EXAMPLE 8–2. For the preceding example, what error in elevation of P would the tilt displacement introduce if the flying height is 12,000 ft.?

By Eq. 5–1,

$$\text{Displacement} = op \cdot h/H$$

$$op = \sqrt{(3.246)^2 + (2.307)^2} = 3.982 \text{ in.}$$

* The line which contains o and v.

Then

$$h = \frac{12,000}{3.982} \times 0.0505 = 152 \text{ ft. error introduced}$$

EXAMPLE 8–3. Determine the error in direction of p introduced by the tilt in Example 8–1.

	x	y
Original coordinates . . .	+3.246	+2.307
Corrections	0.040	0.031
Corrected coordinates . . .	+3.286	| 2.338

Direction on tilted photograph: $\tan = \dfrac{3.246}{2.307} = 1.40702 \quad 54° \, 36'$

Direction on untilted photograph: $\tan = \dfrac{3.286}{2.338} = 1.40547 \quad 54° \, 34'$

Error: 02'

Examples 8–2 and 8–3 serve to emphasize that the effect of tilt is usually much more serious in determining elevations than directions.

8–3. Isocenter. It was found in Art. 5–4 that relief displacements are radial from the nadir point. It will now be shown that the displacements resulting from tilt radiate from the point i (Fig. 8–1), which is that point on the principal line at the intersection of the tilted and horizontal photographs. If this is the center of tilt distortion, then angle $a_1 i a$, designated as θ, will be equal to angle $a'_1 i a'$, designated as θ'.

The following may be written from similar triangles:

$$\frac{a_1 a}{a'_1 a'} = \frac{L a_1}{L a'_1}$$

Also,

$$L a_1 = f \sec \alpha_0 \qquad \text{and} \qquad L a'_1 = f \sec (\alpha_0 + t)$$

So,

$$\frac{a_1 a}{a'_1 a'} = \frac{f \sec \alpha_0}{f \sec (\alpha_0 + t)} = \frac{\cos (\alpha_0 + t)}{\cos \alpha_0} \tag{8–5}$$

In triangle $i a_1 a'_1$, by the law of sines,

$$\frac{i a_1}{i a_1'} = \frac{\sin (90° - \alpha_0 - t)}{\sin (90° + \alpha_0)} = \frac{\cos (\alpha_0 + t)}{\cos \alpha_0} \tag{8–6}$$

Equating 8–5 and 8–6,

$$\frac{a_1 a}{a'_1 a'} = \frac{i a_1}{i a'_1} \qquad \text{or} \qquad \frac{a_1 a}{i a_1} = \frac{a'_1 a'}{i a'_1}$$

But

$$\tan \theta = \frac{a_1 a}{i a_1} \qquad \text{and} \qquad \tan \theta' = \frac{a'_1 a'}{i a'_1}$$

Therefore $\theta = \theta'$, showing that the direction of a from i with respect to the principal plane is the same whether measured on the tilted or the untilted photograph. It follows that all angles measured at the point i are correct in so far as tilt is concerned. This point is called the *isocenter*, or the center of tilt distortion.

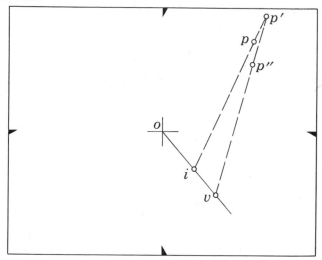

FIG. 8–2. Image displacements, exaggerated. Tilt correction pp' radiates from i while the relief displacement $p'p''$ is radial from v.

8–4. Combined Displacements. Unfortunately, the centers of radiation do not coincide for both tilt and relief displacements, nor is there any third point from which the combined distortions for all points can be said to radiate. The two may be treated in separate calculations or constructions, obtaining a correction for tilt radial from the isocenter and one for relief radial from the nadir point. Such a construction, with values greatly exaggerated, is shown in Fig. 8–2.

8–5. Axes. It is to be remembered in making any numerical calculations based on the preceding theory that the y-axis of reference is the principal line and not the geometrical axis of the photograph. The geometrical axes of the actual photograph are not indicated on Fig. 8–1 and would have no necessary relation to the direction of tilt.

8–6. Tilt Circle. The component of tilt in any direction on the photograph varies from t along the principal line to zero at right angles to it. In general, at any angle θ (Fig. 8–3), the component t' is given by

$$\sin t' = aa''/ia$$

Also,

$$\sin t = a_1 a''_1 / ia_1 \qquad \text{and} \qquad ia_1 = ia \cos \theta$$

By substitution and combination, and noting that $aa'' = a_1 a''_1$, $\sin t' = \sin t \cos \theta$ which, for the usual small values of tilt, may be written $t' = t \cos \theta$. It will be seen that this is the equation of a circle passing through the isocenter and having a diameter lying along the principal line. If the diameter is drawn to a convenient linear scale, then any chord through the isocenter gives the component of tilt for that particular direction.

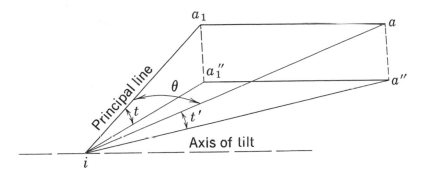

FIG. 8–3. Component of tilt in any direction.

EXAMPLE 8–4. The tilt of an aerial photograph is 3° 18′. (a) What is the component of tilt at 50° from the principal line? (b) At what angle is the tilt 1° 00′?

a. $t' = t \cos 50° = 198 \times 0.64279 = 127'$ or $2° 07'$

b. $\cos \theta = \dfrac{t'}{t} = \dfrac{60}{198} = 0.30303$

$\theta = 72° 22'$

EXAMPLE 8–5. The component of tilt at 135° clockwise from the $+y$ axis is $+0° 50'$, that at 30° is $+1° 30'$. Determine the maximum tilt and its direction.

Let t_1 and t_2 be the two known tilts at angles θ_1 and θ_2 with the principal line (Fig. 8–4), and let $\theta_1 + \theta_2 = \phi$. Then $t_1 = t \cos \theta_1$, $t_2 = t \cos \theta_2$, and $\theta_1 = \phi - \theta_2$

$$\cos \theta_1 = \frac{t_1}{t_2} \times \cos \theta_2 = \cos (\phi - \theta_2) = \cos \phi \cos \theta_2 + \sin \phi \sin \theta_2$$

$$\cos \theta_2 \left(\frac{t_1}{t_2} - \cos \phi \right) = \sin \theta_2 \sin \phi$$

So

$$\frac{\sin \theta_2}{\cos \theta_2} = \tan \theta_2 = \frac{t_1/t_2 - \cos \phi}{\sin \phi}$$

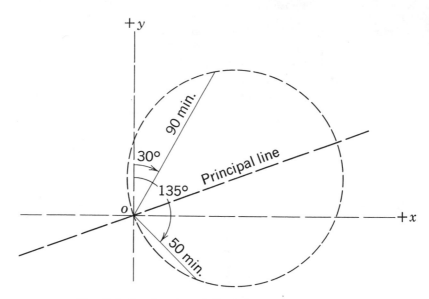

FIG. 8–4. Construction of tilt circle (see Example 8–5).

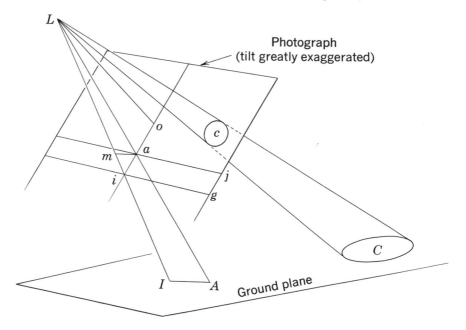

FIG. 8–5. Scale variation on tilted photograph.

Substituting numerical values, $\phi = 135° - 30° = 105°$. Then

$$\tan \theta_2 = \frac{\frac{90}{50} - (-0.25882)}{0.96593} = \frac{2.05882}{0.96593} = 2.13144$$

$$\theta_2 = 64° \; 52'$$

$$\theta_1 = 40° \; 08'$$

Then

$$t = \frac{t_1}{\cos \theta_1} = \frac{90}{0.76455} = 117.7 \text{ or } 1° \; 57'.7$$

and

$$\text{Direction of principal line} = 40° \; 08' + 30° \; 00' = 70° \; 08'$$

8–7. Scale-Point Theory. Consider a tilted photograph and the horizontal ground plane, as shown in Fig. 8–5. The circle c on the photograph will be projected on the ground as the ellipse C. Then the ratio of corresponding diameters of C and c represents the scale of the photograph, but this will vary, depending upon which diameter is taken. If the circle is now made smaller and smaller, it will be seen that the scale at a point of the tilted photograph is not uniform but that it differs with direction. In the following discussion, however, it is said that the scale at any point is its value in the direction of zero tilt, that is, perpendicular to the principal line. Using this conception of scale, then the scale of any line is found to be equivalent to that of some certain point on the line. This is called its "scale point" and the method of locating it is described below.

8–8. Equal-Scale Lines. Let a be a point on the principal line, one unit distant from i. IA in the ground plane then represents the scale of the line ia. If am is constructed horizontally, IA/am is the scale for all lines lying in the horizontal plane maj, and since $am = ia$, this is likewise the scale of ia. In other words, the scale of any line which has one end at the isocenter is equal to the point scale at its other end. The line aj represents a line of equal scale on the photograph and, because of the perspective projection, should be slightly curved toward the axis ig. For small tilts, however, this curve is negligible.

8–9. Scale Variation. For small tilts it can be assumed that the scale, expressed in feet per inch, changes at a uniform rate along the principal line. Thus, if S is the scale at the isocenter, the scales at successive unit distances may be written $S + r$, $S + 2r$, $S + 3r$, ..., $S + nr$. The corresponding ground distances from the isocenter to these points then are $1(S + r)$, $2(S + 2r) = 2S + 4r$, $3(S + 3r) = 3S + 9r$, ..., $n(S + nr) = nS + n^2r$.

The ground distance for a line between two points n_1 and n_2 is

$$(n_2 S + n_2^2 r) - (n_1 S + n_1^2 r) = (n_2 - n_1)S + (n_2^2 - n_1^2)r$$
$$= (n_2 - n_1)S + (n_2 - n_1)(n_2 + n_1)r$$
$$= (n_2 - n_1)[S + (n_2 + n_1)r]$$

It will be seen that the part in brackets is the scale of the line and that it is equal to the scale at the point $(n_2 + n_1)$, that is, the point which is as far from n_2 as the isocenter is from n_1. In other words, the isocenter and the scale point are symmetrical with respect to the line itself.

8–10. Scale-Point Rule. While the above determines the scale-point location only for lines in the direction of maximum tilt, a similar development can be made for a line in any other direction on the photograph by projecting it *horizontally* into the plane containing the line Li. Thus, the rule to determine the scale point of any given line on the photograph may be stated: Drop a perpendicular from the isocenter to the line (produced if necessary); measure the distance from this foot to one end of the line and lay off this same distance in the opposite direction from the other end; this locates the scale point for the line. The application of this rule is shown in Fig. 8–6.

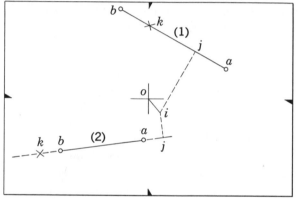

a and b = ends of line

j = foot of perpendicular
   from isocenter

bk made equal to aj

k = scale point for
   line ab

Fig. 8–6. Determination of scale point (1) where perpendicular falls on the line, (2) where perpendicular falls outside the line.

It should be recalled that the scale-point theory here developed is for level ground and cannot be applied without some modification to terrain having topographic relief. This procedure is developed in Chapter 10.

PROBLEMS

8–1. The following photograph coordinates are measured with respect to the principal point as origin and the principal line as y-axis, the nadir point being in the negative direction. For each point, calculate the image displacement resulting from tilt if the focal length is 10 in. and the photograph is tilted 3° 50′.

Point	x (in.)	y (in.)
a	+2.792	+3.256
b	−3.860	+1.704
c	+2.995	−3.902
d	−4.174	−3.728

8–2. Determine the elevation error that is introduced by the tilt in Prob. 8–1 for each of the points if the flying height is 6000 ft.

8–3. Determine the error in direction introduced by tilt for each point of Prob. 8–1.

8–4. Same as Prob. 8–2, but for a flying height of 15,000 ft.

8–5. Same as Prob. 8–1, but for a tilt of 5° 00′.

8–6. Same as Prob. 8–2, but for a tilt of 5° 00′.

8–7. Same as Prob. 8–3, but for a tilt of 5° 00′.

8–8. Same as Prob. 8–4, but for a tilt of 5° 00′.

8–9. Same as Prob. 8–1, but for a focal length of 6 in.

8–10. Same as Prob. 8–2, but for a focal length of 6 in.

8–11. Same as Prob. 8–3, but for a focal length of 6 in.

8–12. Same as Prob. 8–4, but for a focal length of 6 in.

8–13. Compute the amount and direction of the combined tilt and relief displacements for the points of (a) Prob. 8–1 and (b) Prob. 8–2, the elevations being as follows: *a*, 500 ft.; *b*, 1200 ft.; *c*, 1500 ft.; *d*, 2000 ft.

8–14. Compute the amount and direction of the combined tilt and relief displacements for the points of (a) Prob. 8–5 and (b) Prob. 8–6, the elevations being as follows: *a*, 500 ft.; *b*, 1200 ft.; *c*, 1500 ft.; *d*, 2000 ft.

8–15. Compute the amount and direction of the combined tilt and relief displacements for the points of (a) Prob. 8–9 and (b) Prob. 8–10, the elevations being as follows: *a*, 500 ft; *b*, 1200 ft.; *c*, 1500 ft.; *d*, 2000 ft.

8–16. For the photograph in Prob. 8–1, determine the amount of tilt at 30° from the principal line; at 60°; at 100°; at 200°; at 310°.

8–17. For the photograph in Prob. 8–5, determine the amount of tilt at 30° from the principal line; at 60°; at 100°; at 200°; at 310°.

8–18. For the photograph in Prob. 8–5, at what angle with the principal line is the tilt component 1°? 2°? 3°? 4°?

8–19. For a certain photograph, the component of tilt at 40° clockwise from the +*y* axis is +3° 42′; at 150° it is +1° 18′. Determine the maximum tilt and its direction.

8–20. The component of tilt at an angle of 175° clockwise from the +*y* axis is +0° 52′; at 290° it is +3° 10′. Determine the maximum tilt and its direction.

8–21. The maximum tilt of a photograph is known to be 5° 00′. At an angle of 75° clockwise from the +*y* axis, the component is 3° 15′. What is the direction of the maximum tilt?

8–22. The maximum tilt of a photograph is at an angle of 160° clockwise from the +*y* axis, the component at 210° is 2° 40′. Determine the maximum tilt.

9

PRECISE DETERMINATION OF TILT

9–1. Exposure Station. The exposure station of an aerial photograph, i.e., the point in space occupied by the camera at the instant the picture was taken, can be accurately determined, provided sufficient ground control appears in the area of the photograph.

9–2. Approximate Values. Were the photograph absolutely without tilt, the horizontal position of the exposure station could be determined by applying the surveying method of the three-point problem, assuming that at least three well-spaced control points are available. Angles subtended by these points at the center of the photograph can be determined from the photograph itself, and the position of the photograph center can be found either by calculation or by graphical resection. This will be correct only for an untilted photograph, although if the tilt is not large and only horizontal positions are required, errors introduced in subsequent mapping are usually negligible. It may be recalled that this is the basis of the radial-line control methods described in Chapter 6. At any rate, it provides initial trial values for the more precise method presently to be described. With horizontal position determined, the vertical or Z-coordinate for the exposure station of the untilted photograph can be found by using the relation developed in Art. 2–12,

$$H = f \cdot \frac{VP}{vp} + h$$

where H is the Z-coordinate.

9–3. Control. The precise method,* and incidentally one that is valid regardless of the amount of tilt, also utilizes three ground control points which, for best results, should be well separated over the photograph in approximately an equilateral triangle. In practice, of course, it may often be necessary to use points which do not conform to this ideal situation.

9–4. Coordinates. Assume that for the control points A, B, and C, the images a, b, and c on the photograph have been marked and that their

---

* This is but one of a number of analytical methods for determining the exposure station and orientation of an aerial photograph. It is essentially that devised by Professor Earl Church and is based on the Newton method of successive approximations. While any of these become rather tedious with ordinary calculation methods, they are readily adapted to electronic digital computers.

coordinates have been measured with respect to the photograph axes (Fig. 9–1). This can be done precisely by means of a comparator which utilizes microscopes for setting on the points and reading the x- and y-scales. These three points, together with the emergent nodal point L, form a triangular pyramid $Labc$, whose apex angles can be calculated if the focal length f is known (Fig. 9–2). The solution for the exposure station consists in finding a point L in space which, together with the ground points A, B, and C, will form a triangular pyramid $LABC$ whose apex angles have the same values as those of the photo-pyramid.

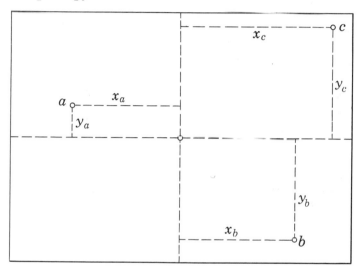

FIG. 9–1. Photograph coordinates of control points.

Let the coordinates on the photograph be designated by $x_a y_a$, $x_b y_b$, and $x_c y_c$, and those on the ground by $x_A y_A z_A$, $x_B y_B z_B$, and $x_C y_C z_C$.

9–5. Photo-pyramid. In the photo-pyramid $Labc$,

$$La = \sqrt{x_a^2 + y_a^2 + f^2} \tag{9–1}$$

and similarly for Lb and Lc.

Also,

$$\cos \alpha = \frac{x_b x_c + y_b y_c + f^2}{Lb \cdot Lc} \tag{9–2}$$

and similarly for $\cos \beta$ and $\cos \gamma$.

While the apex angles α, β, and γ could thus be determined, actually the cosines themselves are sufficient and the angular values need not be found.

9–6. Ground Pyramid. For the ground pyramid $LABC$, the following may be written, the coordinates of L being unknown quantities:

$$LA = \sqrt{(x_L - x_A)^2 + (y_L - y_A)^2 + (z_L - z_A)^2} \tag{9–3}$$

and similarly for LB and LC; also,

$$\cos \alpha = \frac{(x_L - x_B)(x_L - x_C) + (y_L - y_B)(y_L - y_C) + (z_L - z_B)(z_L - z_C)}{LB \cdot LC}$$

$$(9\text{--}4)$$

and similarly for $\cos \beta$ and $\cos \gamma$. The values of $\cos \alpha$, $\cos \beta$, and $\cos \gamma$ are known from Eq. 9–2.

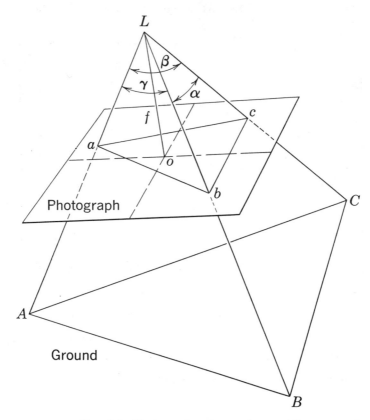

FIG. 9–2. Photograph and ground pyramids.

9–7. Method of Solution. Equations 9–3 and 9–4 together yield three equations in the three unknowns x_L, y_L, and z_L, which are, however, difficult to solve directly. A common method is to assume trial values* for these unknown coordinates, substitute them in the above equations, and find the amounts by which the latter fail to be satisfied. These residuals then serve to determine corrections to the assumed coordinate values. A second set of

---

* Trial values for x_L and y_L may be obtained by a graphical solution of the three-point problem familiar in plane table work, while that for z_L may be obtained from a scale-check solution, as in Art. 5–9.

equations (Eq. 9–5), involving the incremental values Δx_L, Δy_L, and Δz_L, can be written by what is essentially a differentiation of Eq. 9–4. By equating each of these new expressions to its corresponding residual and solving simultaneously, values of Δx_L, Δy_L, and Δz_L are obtained. These are then applied to the assumed coordinates to give closer approximations to the true values of x_L, y_L, and z_L. This procedure is repeated until the residuals become negligible, the final values of x_L, y_L, and z_L then denoting the position of the camera with respect to the ground survey and datum.

9–8. Computations. For ease of expression, let the origin of coordinates be translated to the assumed exposure station and let the values of the coordinates of the control points thus formed be expressed by x'_A, y'_A, z'_A, etc. Then the space distance is

$$(LA) = \sqrt{x'_A{}^2 + y'_A{}^2 + z'_A{}^2} \tag{9–3a}$$

and similarly for (LB) and (LC), the parentheses indicating that they are based on an assumed position of L.

9–9. Residuals. The residuals are calculated by the expressions

$$v_1 = x'_A x'_B + y'_A y'_B + z'_A z'_B - (LA)(LB) \cos \gamma, \text{ etc.} \tag{9–4a}$$

For the small changes in the coordinates of the exposure station represented by Δx_L, Δy_L, and Δz_L, and with simplification by Eq. 9–3a, the method of residuals gives

$$(x'_A + x'_B) \Delta x_L + (y'_A + y'_B) \Delta y_L + (z'_A + z'_B) \Delta z_L$$
$$-\frac{1}{2} \frac{(LB)}{(LA)} (2x'_A \Delta x_L + 2y'_A \Delta y_L + 2z'_A \Delta z_L) \cos \alpha$$
$$-\frac{1}{2} \frac{(LA)}{(LB)} (2x'_B \Delta x_L + 2y'_B \Delta y_L + 2z'_B \Delta z_L) \cos \beta = v_1$$

If $\left[1 - \dfrac{(LA)}{(LB)} \cos \beta \right]$, etc., is represented by $Q_{A/B}$, etc., we have

$$(Q_{B/A} x'_A + Q_{A/B} x'_B) \Delta x_L + (Q_{B/A} y'_A + Q_{A/B} y'_B) \Delta y_L$$
$$+ (Q_{B/A} z'_A + Q_{A/B} z'_B) \Delta z_L = v_1 \tag{9–5}$$

Ordinarily, v_1 would appear in this equation with its sign reversed, but because of the above system of translation of coordinates, the sign of the expression itself is reversed and thus the residual is used with its original sign. Similar equations may be expressed for v_2 and v_3.

9–10. Corrections. Solving these three linear equations simultaneously gives values for Δx_L, Δy_L, and Δz_L, which, when applied to the trial values of the exposure station coordinates, theoretically yield their true values. Actually a second and sometimes a third solution becomes necessary, depending upon the closeness of the original assumptions. However, in these later solutions, it is usually not necessary that new values of Q be determined, these being affected rather slightly by the change in the position of L. This serves to expedite the subsequent solutions.

EXAMPLE 9–1. Following are the photograph and survey coordinates for three control points. Camera focal length is 8.25 in. Find the coordinates of the exposure station.

Point	Survey Coordinates			Photograph Coordinates	
	X (ft.)	Y (ft.)	Z (ft.)	x (in.)	y (in.)
A	24,215	21,605	520	−0.854	+3.916
B	14,011	19,269	946	+4.278	−1.170
C	17,626	28,582	1042	−2.745	−2.512

A rough trial determination gives the following coordinates for (L):

$$18,600 \qquad 23,550 \qquad 12,500$$

The following are obtained by Eqs. 9–1 and 9–2:

$$La = 9.172 \text{ in.} \qquad \cos \alpha = 0.69904$$
$$Lb = 9.367 \text{ in.} \qquad \cos \beta = 0.72970$$
$$Lc = 9.050 \text{ in.} \qquad \cos \gamma = 0.69636$$

By translation of survey coordinates to (L) as origin and by Eq. 9–3a, the following are obtained:

Point	X' (ft.)	Y' (ft.)	Z' (ft.)	(LP) (ft.)
A	+5615	−1945	−11,980	13,373
B	−4589	−4281	−11,554	13,149
C	− 974	+5032	−11,458	12,552

The residuals are now found by Eq. 9–4a:

$$\begin{array}{ccc} +120,976,230 & +115,313,426 & +122,010,590 \\ -122,449,043 & -115,373,931 & -122,485,910 \\ \hline v_1 = - \quad 1,472,813 & v_2 = - \quad 60,505 & v_3 = - \quad 475,320 \end{array}$$

Values of Q and the coefficients of Eqs. 9–5 are formed:

$$Q_{B/A} = +0.31530 \qquad Q_{C/B} = +0.33270 \qquad Q_{A/C} = +0.22257$$
$$Q_{A/B} = +0.29178 \qquad Q_{B/C} = +0.26771 \qquad Q_{C/A} = +0.31510$$

$$\begin{array}{ccc} +1770.4 & - \ 613.3 & -3777.3 \\ -1339.0 & -1249.1 & -3371.2 \\ \hline + \ 431.4 & -1862.4 & -7148.5 \end{array}$$

$$\begin{array}{ccc} -1526.8 & -1424.3 & -3844.0 \\ - \ 260.7 & +1347.1 & -3067.4 \\ \hline -1787.5 & - \quad 77.2 & -6911.4 \end{array}$$

$$\begin{array}{ccc} - \ 216.8 & +1120.0 & -2550.2 \\ +1769.3 & - \ 612.9 & -3774.9 \\ \hline +1552.5 & + \ 507.1 & -6325.1 \end{array}$$

The equations are then solved for ΔX, ΔY, and ΔZ:

$$
\begin{array}{llll}
+\ 431.4\ \Delta X & -1862.4\ \Delta Y & -7148.5\ \Delta Z & +1{,}472{,}813 = 0 \\
-1787.5\ \Delta X & -\ \ 77.2\ \Delta Y & -6911.4\ \Delta Z & +\ \ \ 60{,}505 = 0 \\
+1552.5\ \Delta X & +\ 507.1\ \Delta Y & -6325.1\ \Delta Z & +\ \ 475{,}320 = 0
\end{array}
$$

$$
\begin{array}{llll}
+\ 381.7\ \Delta X & -1647.7\ \Delta Y & -6325.1\ \Delta Z & +1{,}303{,}160 = 0 \\
-1635.9\ \Delta X & -\ \ 70.7\ \Delta Y & -6325.1\ \Delta Z & +\ \ \ 55{,}372 = 0 \\
+1552.5\ \Delta X & +\ 507.1\ \Delta Y & -6325.1\ \Delta Z & +\ \ 475{,}320 = 0
\end{array}
$$

$$
\begin{array}{lll}
+2017.6\ \Delta X & -1577.0\ \Delta Y & +1{,}247{,}788 = 0 \\
+3188.4\ \Delta X & +\ 577.8\ \Delta Y & +\ \ 419{,}948 = 0
\end{array}
$$

$$
\begin{array}{lll}
+\ 739.2\ \Delta X & -\ 577.8\ \Delta Y & +\ \ 457{,}177 = 0 \\
+3188.4\ \Delta X & +\ 577.8\ \Delta Y & +\ \ 419{,}948 - 0
\end{array}
$$

$$
\begin{array}{ll}
+3927.6\ \Delta X & +\ \ 877{,}125 = 0 \\
& \Delta X = -\ \ 223.32
\end{array}
$$

$$
\begin{array}{lll}
-165{,}078 & -\ 577.8\ \Delta Y & +\ \ 457{,}177 = 0 \\
& -\ 577.8\ \Delta Y & +\ \ 292{,}099 = 0 \\
& & \Delta Y = +\ \ 505.54
\end{array}
$$

$$
\begin{array}{llll}
-\ 96{,}340 & -\ 941{,}417 & -7148.5\ \Delta Z & +1{,}472{,}813 = 0 \\
& & -7148.5\ \Delta Z & +\ \ 435{,}056 = 0 \\
& & & \Delta Z = +\ \ 60.86
\end{array}
$$

$$
\begin{array}{llll}
(L) & 18{,}600 & 23{,}550 & 12{,}500 \\
& -\ \ 223 & +\ 506 & +\ \ 61 \\
\hline
& 18{,}377\ \text{ft.} & 24{,}056\ \text{ft.} & 12{,}561\ \text{ft.}
\end{array}
$$

Since these corrections are large, a second solution is made:

Point	X'	Y'	Z'	(LP)
A	+5838	−2451	−12,041	13,604
B	−4366	−4787	−11,615	13,300
C	−751	+4526	−11,519	12,399

$$
\begin{array}{lll}
+126{,}100{,}444 & +115{,}406{,}089 & +123{,}222{,}715 \\
-125{,}994{,}643 & -115{,}276{,}380 & -123{,}082{,}877 \\
\hline
v_1 = +\ \ \ 105{,}801 & v_2 = +\ \ \ 129{,}709 & v_3 = +\ \ \ 139{,}838
\end{array}
$$

Substituting these for the constant terms in the above equations gives $\Delta X = +3.04$ ft., $\Delta Y = +19.80$ ft., $\Delta Z = -19.78$ ft.

$$
\begin{array}{llll}
(L) & 18{,}377 & 24{,}056 & 12{,}561 \\
& +\ \ \ 3 & +\ \ 20 & -\ \ 20 \\
\hline
L & 18{,}380\ \text{ft.} & 24{,}076\ \text{ft.} & 12{,}541\ \text{ft.}
\end{array}
$$

Although a third solution is probably not needed, it should be carried far enough to determine the residuals:

Point	X'	Y'	Z'	(LP)
A	$+5835$	-2471	$-12{,}021$	13,589
B	-4369	-4807	$-11{,}595$	13,291
C	-754	$+4506$	$-11{,}499$	12,373

$+125{,}768{,}477$	$+114{,}964{,}789$	$+122{,}695{,}563$
$-125{,}770{,}555$	$-114{,}956{,}778$	$-122{,}689{,}350$
$v_1 = -\quad 2{,}078$	$v_2 = +\quad 8{,}011$	$v_3 = +\quad 6{,}213$

These are seen to be negligible in the fifth place of numbers and the above coordinates of L will be considered final.

9–11. Tilt. Although several methods have been devised, there is no easy way of precisely determining the tilt of an aerial photograph. The following method, though involving some amount of computation, is probably the most satisfactory for understanding the concepts of the geometry of the photograph.

9–12. Orientation. For the complete orientation of an aerial photograph in space, three quantities are to be calculated:

1. The angle of tilt itself, or the angle t between the camera axis and a truly vertical line.
2. The direction of the line ov on the photograph with respect to its geometric axes. This, expressed as the clockwise angle from the plus y-axis, is commonly called the "swing" s.
3. The azimuth of the principal plane with respect to the ground survey, which will be designated Az_{VO}.

9–13. Tilt and Swing. With the position of L known, the values of the "vertical angles," m_a, m_b, and m_c (Fig. 9–3) can be calculated from the ground pyramid:

$$\cos m_a = \frac{z_L - z_A}{LA}, \text{ etc.} \tag{9–6}$$

Also, from the photograph,

$$\cos m_a = \frac{x_a x_v + y_a y_v + f^2}{La \cdot Lv}$$

and similarly for $\cos m_b$ and $\cos m_c$. Solving these equations for Lv gives

$$Lv = \frac{x_a x_v + y_a y_v + f^2}{La \cos m_a} = \frac{x_b x_v + y_b y_v + f^2}{Lb \cos m_b} = \frac{x_c x_v + y_c y_v + f^2}{Lc \cos m_c} \tag{9–7}$$

yielding two linear equations in x_v and y_v, the solution of which gives the photograph coordinates of the nadir point v. Then

$$\tan t = \frac{\sqrt{x_v^2 + y_v^2}}{f} \tag{9–8}$$

and

$$\tan s = \frac{y_v}{x_v} \tag{9-9}$$

for the first two quantities required.

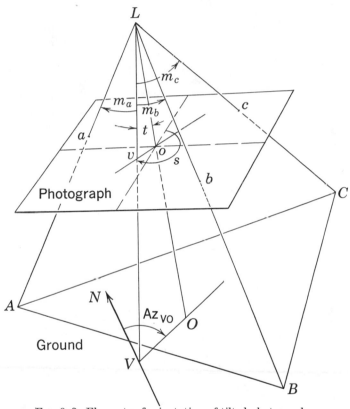

FIG. 9-3. Elements of orientation of tilted photograph.

9-14. Azimuth of Principal Plane. To compute the third quantity, new coordinates $(x'_a,\ y'_a,\ \text{etc.})$ in Fig. 9-4 are determined on the photograph based on v as origin and vo as the direction of the positive y-axis. This may be done by rotation and translation computations of the original coordinates, or they may be measured directly on the photograph after locating the new axes. Then, as shown in Fig. 9-5, the horizontal angle on the photograph between the new y-axis and any line vp is given by

$$\tan \phi_p = \frac{x'_p}{y'_p \cos t} \tag{9-10}$$

If P is a known point, the azimuth of the ground line VP is readily computed from the survey coordinates, V having the same x and y as L. The azimuth of the principal plane (Az_{VO}) is then equal to the azimuth of VP minus ϕ_p. Checks on its value are provided by similar computations for all three points, a, b, and c.

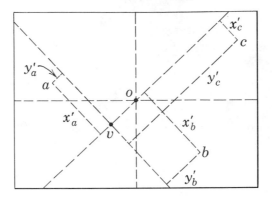

FIG. 9–4. New coordinates based on v as origin and vo as positive y-axis.

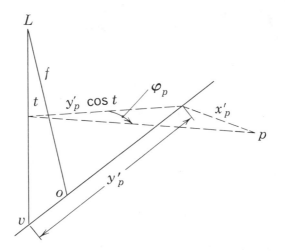

FIG. 9–5. Photograph azimuth.

EXAMPLE. 9–2. Calculate the tilt, swing, and azimuth of the principal plane for the photograph of Example 9–1. By Eqs. 9–6:

$$\cos m_a = \frac{12{,}021}{13{,}589} = 0.88461 \qquad \cos m_b = \frac{11{,}595}{13{,}291} = 0.87239$$

$$\cos m_c = \frac{11{,}499}{12{,}373} = 0.92936$$

Then, by Eq. 9–7, f^2 being $(8.25)^2$, or 68.0625,

$$\frac{-0.854\,x_v + 3.916\,y_v + 68.0625}{8.1136} = \frac{+4.278\,x_v - 1.170\,y_v + 68.0625}{8.1717}$$

$$= \frac{-2.745\,x_v - 2.512\,y_v + 68.0625}{8.4107}$$

from which the following two equations are formed:

$$-6.979\,x_v + 32.000\,y_v + 556.1863 = +34.710\,x_v - 9.493\,y_v + 552.2319$$
$$+35.981\,x_v \quad 9.841\,y_v + 572.4533 - \quad 22.431\,x_v - 20.527\,y_v + 556.1863$$

the solution of which yields the coordinates of the nadir point, v:

$$x_v = -0.2205 \text{ in. and } y_v = -0.3169 \text{ in.}$$

Then

$$ov = \sqrt{(0.2205)^2 + (0.3169)^2} = 0.3861 \text{ in.}$$

$$\tan t = \frac{ov}{f} = \frac{0.3861}{8.25} = 0.04680 \text{ and } t = 2°\,41'$$

$$\tan s = \frac{x_v}{y_v} = \frac{-0.2205}{-0.3169} = 0.69580 \text{ and } s = 214°\,50'$$

The original coordinates of a, b, and c are now rotated and translated to an origin at v and vo as the positive y-axis. These become:

Point	x' (in.)	y' (in.)
a	−2.937	+3.112
b	+4.179	+1.870
c	−0.818	−3.244

and the following calculations determine the azimuth of the principal plane. The agreement among the three values affords a check.

Point	$y'\cos t$	$\tan \phi$	ϕ	$\tan \text{Az}_{LP}$	Az_{LP}	$\text{Az}_{VO} = \text{Az}_{LP} - \phi$
a	+3.109 in.	0.94468	316° 38′	2.36139	112° 57′	156° 19′
b	+1.868 in.	2.23715	65° 55′	0.90888	222° 16′	156° 21′
c	−3.240 in.	0.25247	194° 10′	0.16733	350° 30′	156° 20′
					Average =	156° 20′

9–15. New Points. It may be well to complete this series of calculations by showing the determination of the survey coordinates of a new point P from photograph coordinates on the two overlapping pictures containing the image of the point. The coordinates used are based on the principal line as the y-axis and v as origin, either by direct measurement or by the appropriate transformation if measured from the geometric axes of the photograph.

Then ϕ is calculated from Eq. 9–10 and $\mathrm{Az}_{LP} = \mathrm{Az}_{VO} + \phi_p$, which will give the azimuth from each photograph exposure station to the new point. The intersection of these two lines, obtained by the regular analytic geometry method, will give the horizontal position of the point.

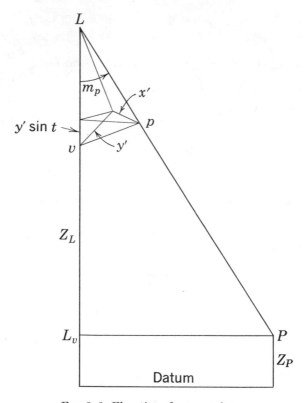

FIG. 9–6. Elevation of a new point.

The vertical angle from the exposure station to the point can be calculated as shown in Fig. 9–6,

$$\cos m_p = \frac{Lv - y' \sin t}{Lp} \qquad (9–11)$$

Lv being $f \sec t$. Then $(Z_L - Z_P) = L_v P \cot m_p$ and

$$Z_P = Z_L - L_v P \cot m_p \qquad (9–12)$$

A determination of Z_P from each exposure station serves as a check.

EXAMPLE 9–3. The coordinates of a point P are to be determined from measurements on photograph No. 1 (this is the one calculated in Examples 9–1 and 9–2) and photograph No. 2, values for which are given here:

L_2: $X = 13,919$ ft. $Y = 26,212$ ft. $Z = 12,623$ ft.

$t = 1° 33'$ $s = 340° 04'$ $Az_{VO} = 273° 49'$

Measurements of P on the two photographs, based on v as origin and vo as the $+y$-axis are:

	X'	Y'
Photo No. 1	+4.434 in.	−1.053 in.
Photo No. 2	−2.493 in.	+0.835 in.

The azimuths from exposure stations to new point are calculated as follows:

Photo	$y' \cos t$	$\tan \phi$	ϕ	$Az_{LP} = Az_{VO} + \phi$
1	1.052 in.	4.21482	103° 21′	259° 41′
2	+0.835 in.	2.98562	288° 31′	202° 20′

Then,

$$\frac{X_P - X_{L_1}}{Y_P - Y_{P_1}} = \tan 259° 41' \qquad \text{and} \qquad \frac{X_P - X_{L_2}}{Y_P - Y_{L_2}} = \tan 202° 20'$$

or

$$18,380 - X = 5.49356 \ (24,076 - Y) = 132,263 - 5.49356 \ Y$$

$$13,919 - X = 0.41081 \ (26,212 - Y) = 10,768 \ - 0.41081 \ Y$$

which, when solved simultaneously, give $X = 12,610$ ft., $Y = 23,026$ ft.

Following are the calculations for the elevation of P:

Photo	$y' \sin t$	$Lv - y' \sin t$	Lp	$\cos m$	m
1	−0.0493 in.	8.3083 in.	9.476 in.	0.87677	28° 45′
2	+0.0226 in.	8.2304 in.	8.640 in.	0.95259	17° 43′

Photo	$\tan m$	LP	$Z_L - Z_P$	Z_P
1	0.54862	5865 ft.	10,690 ft.	1851 ft.
2	0.31946	3444 ft.	10,781 ft.	1842 ft.
			Average =	1846 ft.

It may be pointed out that the horizontal location of P could be determined from one photograph if the elevation of the point were known from some other source.

PROBLEMS

Use these data for the problems which follow:

SURVEY COORDINATES

Point	X (ft.)	Y (ft.)	Z (ft.)
1	12,300	4,917	885
2	4,232	10,509	924
3	4,287	16,238	918
4	12,236	16,341	872
5	4,271	21,512	938
6	14,769	21,710	908

PHOTOGRAPH COORDINATES

	Point	x (mm.)	y (mm.)
Photo I	1	−50.91	−22.62
	2	+ 5.35	+57.69
	4	+63.00	−22.61
Photo II	2	−54.54	+62.48
	3	+ 2.81	+59.99
	4	+ 1.37	−19.40
Photo III	3	−57.28	+66.36
	5	− 4.08	+64.38
	6	− 6.23	−40.93

Camera focal length is 149.4 mm.

9–1. Determine the X, Y, and Z coordinates of the exposure station for Photograph I.

9–2. Calculate the tilt, swing, and azimuth of the principal plane for Photograph I.

9–3. Same as Prob. 9–1 for Photograph II.

9–4. Same as Prob. 9–2 for Photograph II.

9–5. Same as Prob. 9–1 for Photograph III.

9–6. Same as Prob. 9–2 for Photograph III.

9–7. The following coordinates are measured for a new point 101 on Photographs I and II, with v as origin and vo as the positive y-axis. Calculate its survey coordinates.

	x (mm.)	y (mm.)
Photo I	+7.74	+ 3.73
Photo II	−8.12	−52.51

9–8. The following coordinates are measured for a new point 102 on Photographs II and III, with v as origin and vo as the positive y-axis. Calculate its survey coordinates.

	x (mm.)	y (mm.)
Photo II	+20.34	+54.65
Photo III	+ 9.64	+16.20

LABORATORY PROBLEMS

Lab. Prob. 9–1. Select a photograph which contains the images of three well-spaced control points and measure their photographic coordinates. Determine approximate space coordinates for the exposure station and then their exact values.

Lab. Prob. 9–2. Determine the tilt, swing, and azimuth of the principal plane for the photograph of Prob. 9–1.

Lab. Prob. 9–3. Measure the coordinates for several new points whose images appear on both of two adjacent photographs for which the exposure station and orientation have been determined as in Probs. 9–1 and 9–2. Calculate the horizontal position and elevation of each point; compare the elevation with that determined by other methods, if available.

10

TILTED PHOTOGRAPHS

10–1. Scale Affected by Tilt. A method by which ground lines are determined from a single photograph was described in Chapter 5, where it was assumed that the tilt was not large enough to affect the scale in the usable portion of the photograph. With near-perfect flying conditions and with the utmost care in operating the camera, this is indeed possible, but for much otherwise excellent and acceptable photography, tilts are present which, though not excessive, will affect the scale an appreciable amount.

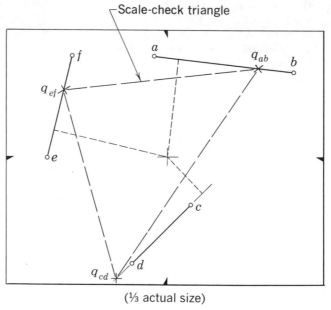

(⅓ actual size)

FIG. 10–1. Three scale-check lines on one photograph.

10–2. Scale-Point Triangle. The scale-point rule of Art. 8–10 provides the basis for a method of utilizing such photographs. Three scale-check lines are used, placed on the photograph so that their scale points form a well-shaped triangle (Fig. 10–1). To correct for the elevations of the ends of the scale-check lines, the relief displacements may be laid off as explained in Art. 5–4, or the following construction may be more convenient.

10–3. Correction for Elevation. In the theory of Art. 8–9 the ground was considered level, but, if the ends of the ground line have different elevations, the inclined plane through these two points may be considered a temporary reference, as shown in Fig. 10–2. Then the computed scale is for the elevation h_M of the point M^* on the reference plane, which corresponds to the scale

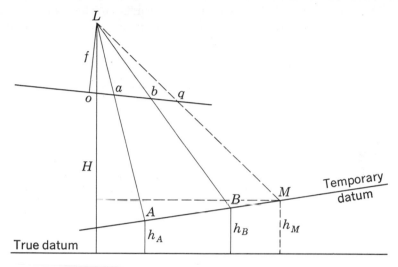

FIG. 10–2. Correction of scale to datum $= h_M/f$.

point on the photograph. After the value of h_M is found by straight proportion, assuming that $BM/bq = AB/ab$, the scale is corrected to the datum as follows:

Scale at the elevation h (see Art. 2–11) is $\dfrac{H - h}{f}$

Scale at datum is $\dfrac{H}{f}$

Difference in scale $= \dfrac{H}{f} - \dfrac{H - h}{f} = \dfrac{H - H + h}{f} = \dfrac{h}{f}$ (10–1)

10–4. Determination of Tilt. For an untilted photograph, the corrected scales as determined by the three scale-check lines should agree. A failure to do so by amounts in excess of those which can reasonably be assigned to errors in measurement therefore indicates the presence of tilt.

The exact determination of the scale points requires that the isocenter be located but this, in turn, cannot be done until the tilt is known. For

---

* It should be realized that the elevation of M is not that of the ground point whose image appears at that place on the photograph. There is in fact no relation whatsoever between them, M being a purely imaginary point whose elevation could differ considerably from that of the actual surface.

small tilts, the principal point may, with negligible error, be used in lieu of the isocenter, while for larger tilts it provides a trial solution from which a nearly correct location of the isocenter can be plotted for a second and more exact solution.

The direction of the tilt axis is determined by plotting a line of equal scale. This may be done by interpolating between two of the scale points for a scale value equal to that of the third scale point. The scale variation

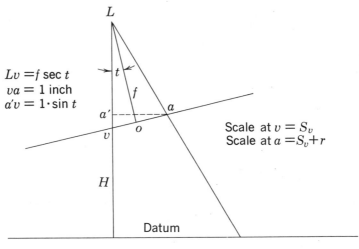

Fig. 10–3.

perpendicular to this direction can then readily be found, and this in turn can be translated into the angle of tilt.

Referring to Fig. 10–3,

$$\text{Scale at the nadir point, } S_v = \frac{H}{f \sec t}$$

$$\text{Scale at 1 inch from the nadir point} = \frac{H}{f \sec t - 1 \cdot \sin t}$$

$$\text{Change in scale per inch } r = \frac{H}{f \sec t - \sin t} - \frac{H}{f \sec t}$$

$$= \frac{Hf \sec t - Hf \sec t + H \sin t}{f \sec t \, (f \sec t - \sin t)} = \frac{H}{f \sec t}\left(\frac{\sin t}{f \sec t - \sin t}\right)$$

For the small values of tilt considered, $\sec t$ may be assumed as 1. Then,

$$r = S_v\left(\frac{\sin t}{f - \sin t}\right)$$

and

$$\frac{f - \sin t}{\sin t} = \frac{S_v}{r} = f \csc t - 1$$

$$\csc t = \frac{1 + (S_v/r)}{f} = \frac{S_v + r}{fr}$$

or

$$\sin t = \frac{fr}{S_v + r} = \frac{fr}{\text{Scale at } 1 \text{ in.}} \qquad (10\text{-}2)$$

For practical purposes the denominator may be taken as the scale at any point near the central portion of the photograph. The isocenter is then located at a distance from the principal point equal to $f \tan \dfrac{t}{2}$.

EXAMPLE 10-1. Determine the axis of tilt and scale variation for the photograph shown in Fig. 10-1, photograph and survey measurements being as follows. Focal length is 8.25 in.

Line	Photograph Length	Ground Length	Point	Elevation
AB	4.263 in.	6735.5 ft.	A	560 ft.
CD	2.486 in.	4052.2 ft.	B	725 ft.
EF	3.122 in.	5004.6 ft.	C	805 ft.
			D	612 ft.
			E	530 ft.
			F	580 ft.

For line AB:

$$\text{Elevation of scale point} = 560 + \frac{(4.26 - 0.75^*)}{4.26} (725 - 560)$$

$$= 560 + 136 = 696 \text{ ft.}$$

$$\text{Scale} = \frac{6735.5}{4.263} + \frac{696}{8.25} = 1580 + 84 = 1664 \text{ ft./in.}$$

For line CD:

$$\text{Elevation of scale point} = 805 - \frac{2.49 + 0.62}{2.49} (805 - 612)$$

$$= 805 - 241 = 564 \text{ ft.}$$

$$\text{Scale} = \frac{4052.2}{2.486} + \frac{564}{8.25} = 1630 + 68 = 1698 \text{ ft./in.}$$

* This and other similar measurements were scaled from the photograph.

For line EF:

$$\text{Elevation of scale point} = 530 + \frac{3.12 - 1.05}{3.12} (580 - 530)$$

$$= 530 + 33 = 563 \text{ ft.}$$

$$\text{Scale} = \frac{5004.6}{3.122} + \frac{563}{8.25} = 1603 + 69 = 1672 \text{ ft./in.}$$

These scales are shown plotted on the photograph in Fig. 10–4.

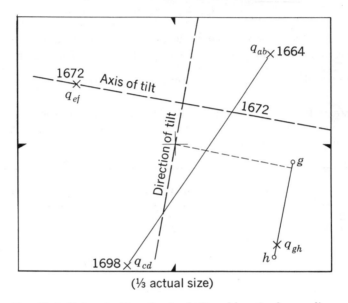

(⅓ actual size)

FIG. 10–4. Determination of axis of tilt and length of a new line.

Interpolating between q_{ab} and q_{cd} for a point whose scale is 1672 ft./in. and connecting this point with q_{ef} gives the direction of the tilt axis:

$$\frac{1698 - 1672}{1698 - 1664} \times 7.62 = 5.83 \text{ in.}$$

The distance from q_{cd} to this line is scaled as 5.30 in., so the scale variation along the principal line is $\frac{26}{5.30} = 4.91$ ft./in. per in.

EXAMPLE 10–2. For the photograph of Example 10–1, determine the angle of tilt and the location of the isocenter.

$$\sin t = \frac{8.25 \times 4.91}{1672} = 0.02423$$

$$t = 1° \ 23'$$

$$oi = f \tan t/2 = 8.25 \times 0.01208 = 0.100 \text{ in.}$$

10–5. New Lines. The determination of the ground length of a new line involves the construction to locate its scale point, finding the value of the scale at that point, correcting it for elevation, and then multiplying this corrected scale by the photograph distance.

EXAMPLE 10–3. From the photograph of Example 10–1, find the length of line GH, its photograph distance being 3.295 in. The elevations of G and H are 660 ft. and 920 ft., respectively.

$$\text{Elevation of scale point} = 920 - \frac{3.30 - 2.94}{3.30} (920 - 660)$$

$$= 920 - 28 = 892 \text{ ft.}$$

q_{gh} is scaled as 4.00 in. from the 1672 scale line.
Change in scale $= 4.91 \times 4.00 = 19.6$ ft./in.
Scale at $q_{gh} = 1672 + 20 = 1692$ ft./in.

Correction for elevation $= \dfrac{892}{8.25} = 108$

Scale of line $GH = 1692 - 108 = 1584$ ft./in.
Ground length $= 3.295 \times 1584 = 5219$ ft.

While Figs. 10–1 and 10–4 indicate that the constructions and measurements were made on the front of the photograph, in actual practice they may more commonly be made either on an overlay or on the back of the photograph itself.

10–6. Bridging Across Control. In a project covering an extended area, the procedure described above requiring three control lines on each photograph used would entail control surveying not only in large amounts but very probably in difficult or awkward locations. This situation can be obviated by a method of "bridging" across several photographs from one set of control lines to another, transferring scale from one photograph to the next, utilizing the 60 per cent overlap of successive pictures.

It should be possible to locate three lines within the overlap such that their scale points on the second photograph determine a nearly equilateral triangle (Fig. 10–5). While their elevations would be needed, the points defining the lines would not have to be identified on the ground. The ground lengths of the three lines can then be determined from the controlled photograph and used in turn to calculate scales on the second, thus determining its axis of tilt and scale variation. This process can be continued from picture to picture to the next fully controlled photograph, any discrepancies which then become apparent being distributed back through the flight.

10–7. Eliminating Need for Elevation. An objection to this procedure is that the elevation of each point must be known. However, the effects of elevation can be eliminated if the lines are selected as shown in Fig. 10–6. It will be noted that the lines are perpendicular to o_1o_2, which joins the conjugate centers, and have one end on or very close to that line. Thus, for

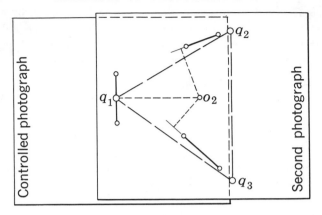

FIG. 10–5. Carrying scale to adjacent photograph, elevations known.

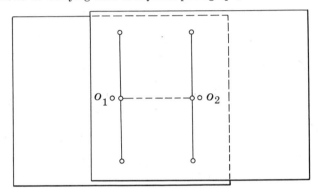

FIG. 10–6. Carrying scale to adjacent photograph, elevations not needed.

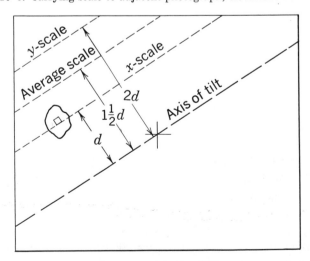

FIG. 10–7. Photograph scale for area.

practical purposes, the "outside" point of each line is also its scale point. Furthermore, from their similar location with respect to o_1o_2, the elevation correction will be the same for both photographs. Therefore, the scales of the second photograph can be determined by direct comparison of the lengths of the lines on the two pictures without obtaining either the elevations or ground distances. Of course, wherever ground distances are required for any lines, elevations are still necessary.

10–8. Area Scales. A rapid method of determining areas is to planimeter them directly on the photograph, assuming that their boundaries can be identified, and to multiply these values by the proper photograph scales. Fig. 10–7 shows an irregular area on a photograph for which the tilt has been determined. Let the area be divided into a large number of small squares, one of which is shown, with sides parallel and perpendicular to the tilt axis. The scale for the parallel side (x-scale in the figure) is that of the line of equal scale of which it is a segment, while the scale of the perpendicular side (y-scale) is that of a line twice as far from the tilt axis. Then the average scale for the square is that for a point halfway between these, or one and one-half times the distance the square is from the axis. The same rule can be applied to the entire area, since it is composed of a large number of squares.

10–9. Tilt Zones. A convenient way of designating these area scales is to plot zones, the boundary lines of which are parallel to the tilt axis and spaced to give any desired increment of scale change. These zone lines will be spaced at $d/1.5d = 2/3$ the interval for the corresponding linear scale change. It should be noted that the term *area scale* is really an *average linear* scale for the area and must be used accordingly.

EXAMPLE 10–4. Referring to the photograph of Example 10–1, determine the spacing of area correction zone lines for a scale increment of 10 ft./in.

From Example 10–1, the scale variation was found to be 4.91 ft./in. per in. Then the spacing for a *linear* scale increment of 10 ft./in. is $10/4.91 = 2.037$ in. and that for the same *area* scale increment is $2/3 \times 2.037 = 1.358$ in. The central zone could be established symmetrical with the principal point (or isocenter for larger tilts), and its boundaries would be $\frac{1}{2} \times 1.358 = 0.679$ in. from the tilt axis, as shown in Fig. 10–8.

EXAMPLE 10–5. The planimetered area for a field on the photograph of Example 10–1 is 0.532 sq. in., the center of the field lying about 3 inches from the tilt axis, as shown at F in Fig. 10–8. Determine the area of the field in acres.

It is seen from Fig. 10–8 that the field is in the 1698-scale zone, and, because it is on the "high" side of the zone, the scale may be taken as 1700 ft./in.

$$\text{Area} = 0.532 \times (1700)^2 = 1,537,480 \text{ sq. ft.} = 35.30 \text{ acres.}$$

10–10. Relief Zones. The foregoing method is correct only for relatively flat terrain at the datum level so that appropriate elevation corrections must be made if topographic relief is present. The photographs may be zoned for relief as well as for tilt, provided a suitable contour map of the area or sufficient spot elevations are available. The zoning contour interval is given

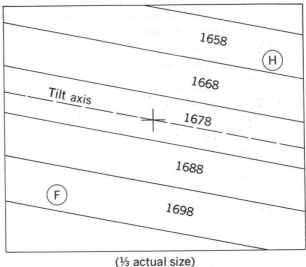

(⅓ actual size)

FIG. 10–8. Area scale zoning for tilt. Scales shown are in feet per inch for datum elevation.

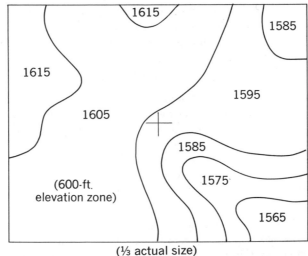

(⅓ actual size)

FIG. 10–9. Zoning for scale due to relief. Scales shown are in feet per inch.

by h = scale increment $\times f$, the scale increment used being the same as for tilt.

EXAMPLE 10–6. For the photograph of Example 10–1, determine the contour interval for relief zoning, using 10 ft./in. increments.

Contour interval, $h = 10 \times 8.25 = 82.5$ ft.

Starting with a zone which most nearly represents the ground elevation of the greater part of the photograph, the contours at this calculated interval are drawn both above and below as necessary to cover the usable part of the picture. Fig. 10–9 shows this zoning at the interval calculated in Example 10–6. The scale for the basic elevation zone is equal to the datum scale at the center of the photograph minus the scale correction for the basic elevation used. In the above example, the basic elevation was taken as 600 ft., so the scale for this zone is $1678 - \dfrac{600}{8.25} = 1605$ ft./in. The zones for relief and for tilt may be combined as shown in Fig. 10–10.

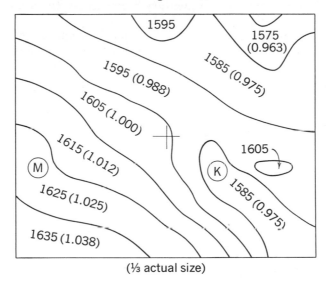

(⅓ actual size)

FIG. 10–10. Combined tilt and relief zones, showing scales in feet per inch. Numbers in parentheses are area ratios.

10–11. Enlargements and Area Ratios. It may be easier for boundary identifications and for planimetering to work on a photograph of larger scale, which may be of some specified value. Furthermore, the zones may be designated by area ratios rather than directly in scale values.

EXAMPLE 10–7. Calculate the ratio of enlargement of the photograph of Example 10–1 to give a basic scale of 660 ft./in. Also calculate the area ratio of each zone, the 660 zone being unity.

$$\text{Ratio of enlargement} = \frac{1605}{660} = 2.432$$

$$\text{Area ratio} = \left(\frac{1615}{1605}\right)^2 = 1.0125$$

and similarly for the other zones. For practical purposes, the ratio may be considered to vary uniformly and the successive ratios obtained by addition or subtraction of a constant (0.0125 in this example). These ratios are shown in parentheses in Fig. 10–10.

EXAMPLE 10–8. The planimetered area of a field located at K (Fig. 10–10) on the enlargement as calculated in Example 10–7 is 0.826 sq. in. Determine the area in acres.

From Fig. 10–10, the field is in the 0.975 ratio zone.

$$\text{Area} = 0.826 \times (660)^2 \times 0.975 = 350,810 \text{ sq. ft.} = 8.054 \text{ acres}$$

Tilt Correction in Elementary Stereoscopic Devices

10–12. Effect of Tilt. Elementary devices for determining elevations and contours by the stereoscopic observation of overlapping photographs were described in Chapter 7. It was assumed that the photographs were truly

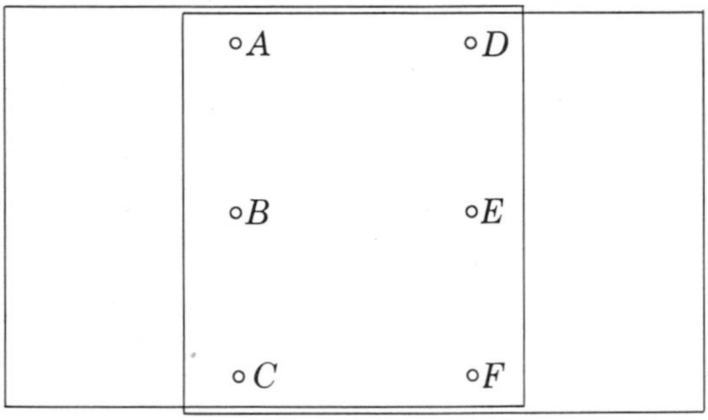

FIG. 10–11. Overlapping area of two photographs with locations of points of known elevation.

vertical, which may well be true for the photography of an area as a whole, the average tilt for a large number of photographs often being practically negligible. However, there are sometimes individual photographs for which the tilts, though within specifications, may be large enough to affect seriously the accuracy of the elevations or contours.

10–13. Parallax Corrections. Corrections for tilt may be determined for a pair of photographs, provided elevations are known for about five or six points well distributed through the overlapping area. Let A, B, C, D, E, and F in Fig. 10–11 be points whose elevations are known and whose images can be identified. If one of them is used as a base point, Δh to each of the other points can be obtained by subtraction and Δp calculated by Eq. 7–6. Also, a value for Δp can be obtained by direct measurement on the photographs. Any discrepancies between these calculated and measured values are attributed to a combination of tilts in the two photographs and provide a means of determining corrections for the entire area of overlap.

EXAMPLE 10–9. Calculate the parallax corrections for points having elevations and scale readings as given in the following table. $H = 10,000$ ft., $B = 4000$ ft., and $f = 210$ mm.

Point	Elevation (ft.)	Δh* (ft.)	Theoretical Δp (mm.)	Scale Reading (mm.)	Measured Δp (mm.)	Correction (mm.)
A	1200	500	5.13	23.32	5.08	+0.05
B	850	150	1.48	19.76	1.52	−0.04
C	1480	780	8.26	26.62	8.38	−0.12
D	1020	320	3.22	21.36	3.12	+0.10
E	700	0	–	18.24	–	0
F	940	240	2.39	20.70	2.46	−0.07

* Calculated from the lowest point.

10–14. Correction Lines. These corrections are then marked at their

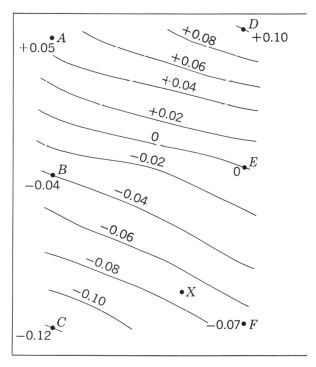

FIG. 10–12. Construction of correction lines on right-hand photograph of the pair in Fig. 10–11.

respective points on one of the photographs, as shown in Fig. 10–12, and correction lines are drawn by interpolation. Although these correction lines are placed on only one of the photographs of the overlap, it is to be noted that they apply to the two photographs as a unit. Either photograph when combined with the next one of its flight will probably yield an entirely different pattern.

10–15. Elevations. For the determination of a new elevation, a parallax reading is taken on the desired point in the usual way and then corrected by a value read from the nearest correction line on the marked photograph. Using the corrected reading, Δp is obtained by subtraction, Δh is calculated, and the elevation of the point is determined. This procedure is illustrated in the following example.

EXAMPLE 10–10. Calculate the elevation of point X (Fig. 10–12), the scale reading for which is 22.58 mm. By inspection, the correction at X is -0.07 mm., so the corrected reading is 22.51 mm.

Then
$$\Delta h = \frac{(10,000 - 700)^2 (22.51 - 18.24)}{4000 \times 210} = +440 \text{ ft.}$$

$$\text{Elevation of } E = \quad 700 \text{ ft.}$$
$$\text{Elevation of } X = \quad 1140 \text{ ft.}$$

A second solution, using the new elevation, gives $\Delta h = 419$, making the elevation of $X = 1119$ ft.

10–16. Contours. It will be recalled that in contouring, the reading for the desired contour elevation is first calculated and then set off on the scale, after which the instrument is moved over the photograph until the floating mark appears to rest upon the ground. By keeping the mark in apparent contact with the ground, the contour is traced to the scale of the photograph for that particular elevation. When correction lines are used, this same procedure is followed, except that the setting is changed each time a correction line is crossed. It should be noted that the corrections for this operation will be applied with the opposite sign, since a calculated reading is to be changed to that actually used on the photographs.

PROBLEMS

10–1. The ground distance of a line AB is 4750 ft., the photograph distance ab is 2.130 in. The elevation of A is 385 ft. and that of B is 840 ft. Focal length of the camera is 8.25 in. The perpendicular from the principal point to the line ab falls 0.72 in. from a toward b. Calculate the datum scale determined by this line.

10–2. Same as Prob. 10–1, except the foot of the perpendicular falls 0.55 in. from b toward a.

10–3. Same as Prob. 10–1, except the foot of the perpendicular falls 1.28 in. from a in the opposite direction from b.

10–4. Same as Prob. 10–1, except the foot of the perpendicular falls 1.64 in. from b in the opposite direction from a.

10–5. The following coordinates are measured for points on a photograph whose focal length is 10 in.

Point	x (in.)	y (in.)
a	−3.00	+4.00
b	+1.00	+4.00
c	−4.00	−1.00
d	−4.00	−4.00
e	0	−4.00
f	+4.00	0

Ground distances and elevations are as follows:

$$AB = 8160 \text{ ft.} \qquad A = 1150 \text{ ft.} \qquad B = 1260 \text{ ft.}$$
$$CD = 5910 \text{ ft.} \qquad C = 1085 \text{ ft.} \qquad D = 940 \text{ ft.}$$
$$EF = 11{,}380 \text{ ft.} \qquad E = 915 \text{ ft.} \qquad F = 1130 \text{ ft.}$$

Determine the axis of tilt and the scale variation.

10–6. For the photograph of Prob. 10–5, determine the angle of tilt and the location of the isocenter.

10–7. For the photograph of Prob. 10–5 calculate the lengths for the traverse $GHJKLMNG$, photograph coordinates and elevations for which are as follows:

Point	x (in.)	y (in.)	Elevation (ft.)
g	−4.00	+2.00	820
h	0	+2.00	900
j	+2.00	0	1100
k	+2.00	−3.00	1040
l	−2.00	−3.00	890
m	−2.00	+1.00	950
n	−4.00	+1.00	870

10–8. For the photograph of Prob. 10–5, determine the spacing of area correction zone lines for a scale increment of 20 ft./in.

10–9. With reference to the photograph of Fig. 10–8, the planimetered area of a field at H is 0.762 sq. in. Determine the area of the field in acres.

10–10. For the photograph of Prob. 10–5, calculate the ratio of enlargement to give a basic scale at the center of 1000 ft./in. Determine the area ratio for each zone determined in Prob. 10–8.

10–11. Referring to the photograph of Fig. 10–10, the area of a field at M as planimetered on the enlargement (660 ft./in. basic scale) is 1.204 sq. in. Determine the area of the field in acres.

10–12. The following scale readings were made with a stereocomparagraph-type instrument on six points spaced as shown in Fig. 10–11. The flying height is 15,000 ft., the base between photograph centers is 5000 ft., and the focal length is 8.250 in. Calculate the parallax correction for each point, and plot correction lines for an interval of 0.002 in.

Point	Elevation (ft.)	Scale Reading (in.)
A	2000	5.488
B	2540	5.602
C	1850	5.438
D	1580	5.393
E	950	5.242
F	1370	5.342

10-13. Calculate the elevations of the points appearing on the photographs of Prob. 10–12, for which the scale readings and locations are as follows:

Location	Scale Reading (in.)
Midway between A and B	5.572
1/4 way from D to E	5.368
1/3 way from C to B.	5.507
Midway between C and F	5.372
1/4 way from E to C	5.302

LABORATORY PROBLEMS

Lab. Prob. 10-1. Select a photograph which contains the images of the terminal points for three ground control lines. Mark these images carefully and measure the lines on the photograph with a finely divided scale. Locate the three scale points, calculate the datum scale for each line, and determine the axis of tilt, the rate of scale variation, and the angle of tilt.

Lab. Prob. 10-2. Choose several new lines on the photograph of Prob. 10–1 for which the elevations of the terminal points are known. Measure the photograph distance, locate the scale point, and calculate the ground distance for each line.

Lab. Prob. 10-3. Draw tilt zone lines on the photograph of Prob. 10–1 for a change of 2 per cent in area scale between adjacent zones. If a topographic map of the area is available, also draw relief zone lines for the same variation of area scale. Combine the two sets of zone lines.

Lab. Prob. 10-4. Mark out several fields in different parts of the photograph of Prob. 10–3. Measure the photographic area of each with a planimeter and calculate the ground area in acres.

Lab. Prob. 10-5. Select two or more consecutive photographs of a flight strip, for which the tilt of one photograph has been determined as in Prob. 10–1. By the procedure outlined in Arts. 10–6 and 10–7, determine the tilts of the other photographs.

Lab. Prob. 10-6. Refer to Probs. 7–3 and 7–4. Select six points in the overlap located about as shown in Fig. 10–11 for which the elevations are known. Calculate the theoretical parallax difference for each point with respect to one of the points as a bench mark, measure the actual parallax difference with the instrument, and note the difference as a correction. On the basis of these, plot correction lines, interpolating as in contouring, for changes of 2 or 5 mm.

Repeat Lab. Probs. 7–3 and 7–4, but this time make corrections for elevations and contours according to the lines just plotted.

11

STEREOSCOPIC PLOTTING INSTRUMENTS

11-1. Automatic Plotters. In addition to the elementary devices described in Chapter 7, there are several other instruments, covering a considerable range of complexity and accuracy, for the production of both planimetric and topographic maps from aerial photographs.

It was found that contours could not be plotted directly with the elementary devices previously discussed because of the change in scale with contour elevation. Also, any allowance for tilt, if made at all, was by a system of correction lines or zones based on several known elevations in each overlap. The instruments presently to be discussed are unhampered by such limitations, being designed to use the photographs completely oriented with respect to tilt and to produce maps to correct scale, including the contours, with no further steps required.

11-2. Kinds of Instruments. The instruments may be divided into two general classes. In one, the photographs are set in holders for stereoscopic viewing after being oriented with respect to each other and to the ground control. A floating mark is formed in one of various ways by the fusion of two separate marks, one in the field of view of each photograph, somewhat as in the simpler stereocomparagraph. In the second class, each of the photographs is projected upon a viewing or plotting table in a different color, with the common areas superimposed upon each other. Stereoscopic vision is then obtained by special viewing spectacles, each lens of which has the same color as the corresponding projected photograph. In this type, the floating mark is at the center of a small stand, which can be moved both horizontally and vertically.

Some of the instruments representing each class are treated in this chapter. It is to be emphasized that the specific instruments mentioned and described have been selected to exemplify the principles on which they operate and are not intended to compare the respective advantages of makes which are competitive in price or productive results. Furthermore, this is not intended as a comprehensive survey of all the equipment available, so that the omission of any particular make or model is not intended to imply any inferiority. Since these instruments are operated by rather highly skilled personnel, the skill increasing of course with the complexity of the

FIG. 11-1. K.E.K. Stereoscopic Plotter. (Courtesy of Philip B. Kail Associates.)

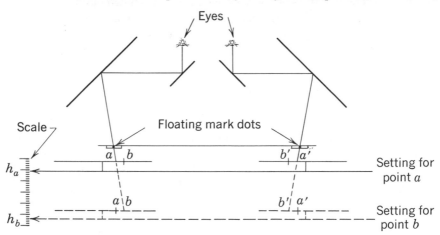

FIG. 11-2. Diagram of K.E.K. Plotter, showing movement of photograph tables for points at different elevations.

equipment, only brief descriptions are given, with no attempt to explain the theories upon which their operations are based.*

11-3. K.E.K. Plotter. The K.E.K.† Stereoscopic Plotter is similar to the radial plotter (Art. 6-20), but the former is equipped with additional movements and parts which provide for drawing contours as well as

---

* Detailed studies of the theory and operation of these instruments are not normally covered in elementary work in photogrammetry.

† J. E. King, J. W. Elliott, and P. B. Kail.

planimetry (Fig. 11–1). It consists principally of a mirror-type stereoscope, photograph holders which are adjustable for rotation about their three axes, and the floating-mark assembly, which is suspended in the space between the photographs and the mirrors. Allowance for change in elevation is provided by a vertical movement of the photograph tables, while the separation of the dots in the floating-mark assembly remains constant after being once set for the desired scale. This is illustrated in Fig. 11–2, which shows the different vertical positions of the photograph holder assembly for the two points a and b. The vertical movement of the holders as indicated by the scale readings is then a measure of the change in elevation.

Since the separation of the dots remains constant, it follows that all plotting, both of contours and planimetry, is done at the same scale, independent of that of the photographs themselves. A drawing arm is attached to the floating-mark assembly, which serves both to maintain parallel motion of the marks in a horizontal plane and to trace the details on the map, enlarged or reduced as necessary by a pantographic arrangement.

11–4. Wernstadt-Mahan Plotter. A similar type of instrument is the Wernstadt-Mahan Plotter, manufactured by Harrison C. Ryker, except that the photograph tables remain stationary and it is the floating-mark assembly that is moved vertically with changes in elevation.

11–5. Zeiss Stereotope. A relatively new development of this type of plotter is the Zeiss Stereotope, shown in Fig. 11–3. The photographs are moved on their carriages underneath the floating-mark plates, which remain stationary in the center of the field of view. Instead of the photographs being set in their relative positions as to tilt, they remain level on the carriages and a correction is made in the parallax reading throughout the area of overlap by means of a so-called computer. With a point at each corner of the model known in elevation, the settings of the computer can be made by calculating the theoretical parallax readings and correcting the observed parallaxes accordingly by means of four correction screws, one for each corner of the model. This might be considered a mechanical and automatic method of applying the adjustments which were made by means of correction graphs for the stereocomparagraph (Art. 10–14). There is an additional correction computer for the variation of scale with contour elevation, and a pantographic correction to provide the desired plotting scale.

11–6. Wild Autograph. An example of one of the more complex and accurate plotting instruments is the Wild A7 Autograph, pictured in Fig. 11–4. The photographs are placed in the holders at the top of the instrument, where they can be rotated about the three axes to assume their correct positions in space. A floating-mark system consists of two measuring marks, one immediately beneath each photograph carrier, which travel parallel to the plane of the photograph. This movement is controlled in the X and Y coordinate directions by the two handwheels at the front of the instrument

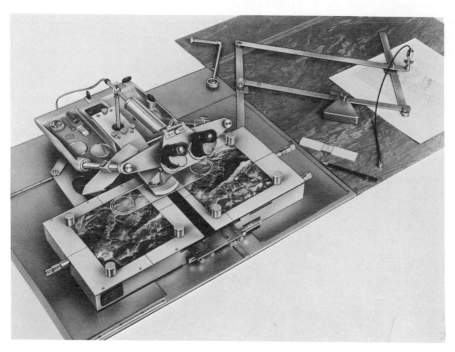

FIG. 11–3. Zeiss Stereotope. (Courtesy of Transmares Corporation.)

FIG. 11–4. The A7 Precision Autograph. (Courtesy of Wild Heerbrugg Instruments, Inc.)

and in the Z direction by the foot wheel near the right leg. These motions are indicated by the operation diagram in Fig. 11–5, and the observation system is shown in Fig. 11–6.

By manipulating the handwheels, the floating mark can be made to follow any path on the model or any particular item of detail that is desired, and these movements are translated to the plotter at the right through a

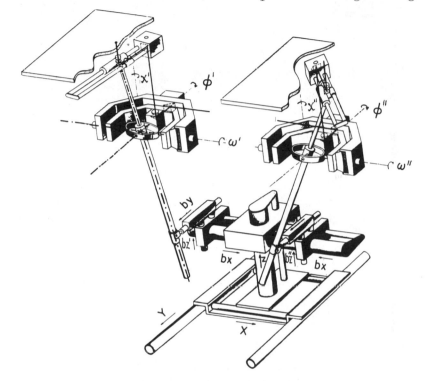

Fig. 11–5. Operation diagram of the Wild A7. (Courtesy of Wild Heerbrugg Instruments, Inc.)

mechanical connection. With the Z motion the mark is kept in apparent contact with the ground surface by varying the lateral separation of its two components. For contour plotting, the Z motion is set at the predetermined reading for the particular contour elevation and locked in that position. The handwheels are then turned until the floating mark appears to rest upon the ground, thus locating a point on the desired contour. By further turning the wheels so that the floating mark is always in apparent contact with the ground, the contour will be traced out and plotted on the map.

Other instruments of similar type include the Zeiss Stereoplanigraph, the Hugerschoff Aerocartograph, the Poivilliers Stereotopograph, and the Wild A8 Stereo-plotting Machine.

FIG. 11-6. Observation system of the Wild A7. (Courtesy of Wild Heerbrugg Instruments, Inc.)

Fig. 11–7. Auxiliary Multiplex projector unit. (Courtesy of Bausch & Lomb Optical Co.)

Stereoprojection Plotters

11–7. Instruments. Some examples of the projection type of stereoscopic plotting instruments are the Multiplex (Fig. 11–7), the Balplex (Fig. 11–8), and the Kelsh Plotter (Fig. 11–9). While these may differ in details of construction and appearance, they all employ the basic principle of projecting

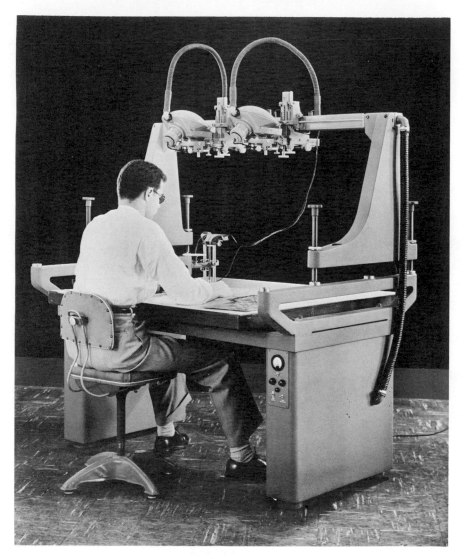

FIG. 11–8. Balplex mapping unit. (Courtesy of Bausch & Lomb Optical Co.)

two overlapping photographs* upon a plotting table, where they are viewed through special spectacles for stereoscopic vision.

11–8. Component Parts. The main components of this type of plotter are: (1) the supporting framework, including plotting table and carrier bar; (2) the units for projecting the photographs, either at the original size or at a

---

* Although this discussion is confined to vertical photography, some of these instruments are adaptable to obliques (see Art. 12–9 *et seq.*).

reduction; (3) a tracing stand with a floating mark for the measurement of elevations and tracing of planimetric details and contours; and (4) spectacles for viewing the projection stereoscopically. A printer for making the reduced plates used in the projection units is shown in Fig. 11–10.

11–9. Projection. The projectors, when correctly placed upon the carrier bar, may be considered as representing the camera in its positions at successive

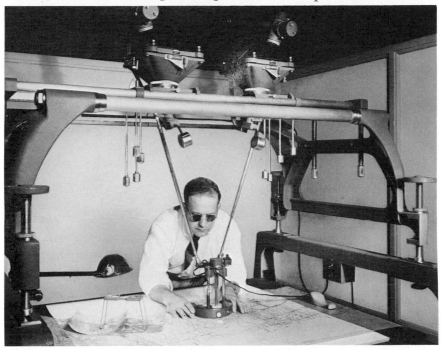

Fig. 11–9. The Kelsh Plotter uses full-scale photographs. Note the guide rods attached to the tracing stand; these rods swing the illuminating lamps above the photographs to follow the movement of the stand. (Courtesy of Air Survey Corporation.)

exposure stations along the flight line. Camera and projectors are optically matched so that the angular relations are exactly reproduced. Thus light rays which originally passed from a ground point to the camera are now exactly projected in the reverse direction.

11–10. Parallax. When two adjacent photographs are correctly projected, the rays to all the corresponding points on the two photographs will intersect in space. The process of effecting this condition is called *relative orientation*. In the projection, consider one particular point, such as the road crossing in Fig. 11–11. At first, the two corresponding images will probably fail to coincide as shown. This parallax* can be resolved into components parallel

* See Art. 7–5 for a treatment of parallax.

FIG. 11–10. The Multiplex and Balplex use reduced photographs in the projectors. This printer reduces the original film to a smaller diapositive. (Courtesy of Bausch & Lomb Optical Co.)

to the two horizontal coordinate axes of the instrument. These components are called the x- and y-parallax. The x-parallax can never be removed simultaneously for all points in the overlap so long as there are any differences in elevation, and it is indeed this very fact that permits the determination of elevations and the delineation of contours. However, the y-parallax can and must be eliminated throughout the overlap so that corresponding images on the two photographs can be made to coincide by only a vertical movement of the tracing stand disk.

11–11. Projector Movements. Each projector (Fig. 11–12) can be moved in six different ways, as follows: (1) X, parallel to the carrier bar, which is in turn parallel, or nearly so, to the flight line; (2) Y, perpendicular to the carrier bar horizontally; (3) Z, a vertical movement; (4) "swing," a rotation

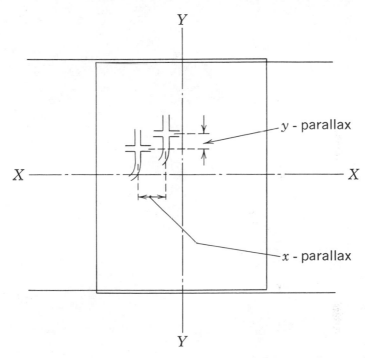

FIG. 11–11. Diagram showing x- and y-parallax of a projected image.

about the vertical axis; (5) "X-tilt," a rotation about the Y-axis; and (6) "Y-tilt," a rotation about the X-axis. The last two are seen to be components of the absolute value of tilt.

11–12. Relative Orientation. These various motions can be used to eliminate the y-parallax in the overlap. Five definite points are selected, spaced about as shown in Fig. 11–13, 1 and 2 being located at or very close to the respective principal points. The projectors are moved in a systematic procedure so that the y-parallax is eliminated from each of the points in turn, that of the previous points being disturbed as little as possible.

It may be seen (Fig. 11–14) that an X motion of the right-hand projector will not affect any of the points in y; a Y motion will directly affect all the points in y; a Z motion will introduce a y displacement in points 3, 4, and 5; swing will cause y movements at points 2, 4, and 5; X-tilt will effect y

FIG. 11–12. One of the projectors for the Balplex Plotter. (Courtesy of Bausch & Lomb Optical Co.)

movements at points 4 and 5; and Y-tilt will move all points in the y direction. Corresponding effects can be written for the various movements of the left projector. With these in mind, the following program may be outlined for the relative orientation.

Let the left projector be designated as I and the right projector as II. The y-parallax at 1 is removed by swinging I; at 2 by swinging II; at 3 by

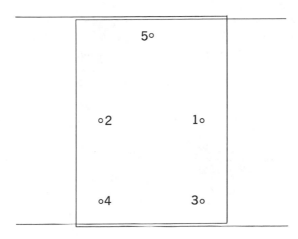

FIG. 11–13. Location of points for relative orientation.

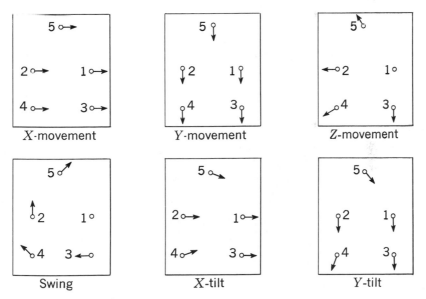

FIG. 11–14. Diagram showing effects on points of the six movements of the right-hand projector.

an X-tilt of I; at 4 by an X-tilt of II; and at 5 by a Y-tilt of either I or II. Since the last movement also affects the y-parallax in the preceding points as well as in 5 itself, an overcorrection must be made of about two and one-half times the original amount. The entire procedure is then repeated until no further adjustment is needed at any point, when it will be found that the y-parallax is eliminated for the entire area of overlap.

11–13. Tracing Stand. The tracing stand (Fig. 11–15) consists of a supporting yoke bearing a circular disk on a vertical shaft which can be raised and lowered by an attached screw. The stand is supported on bearings so that it can readily be moved over the plotting surface. A hole in the

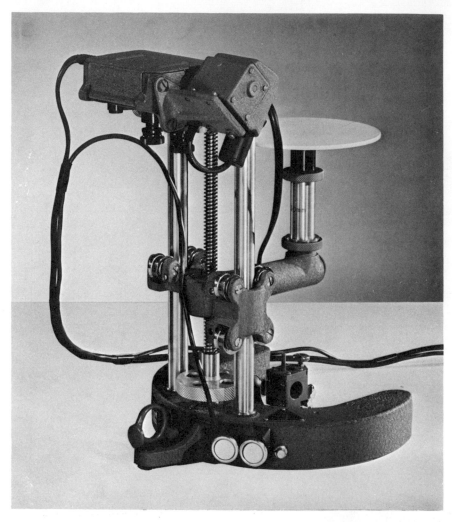

FIG. 11–15. Tracing stand. (Courtesy of Bausch & Lomb Optical Co.)

center of the disk, illuminated by a small lamp beneath, forms a floating mark, vertically below which is a pencil point that can be raised from the paper when not in use. The disk, being some 4 inches in diameter, provides sufficient space for stereoscopic viewing of a small area of the overlapping projections. The floating mark can be set on any desired point by moving the stand over the table horizontally and the disk vertically, until the mark appears to rest directly at the point, the vertical movement being measured by a scale or counter. When the floating mark is thus set on a point of the stereoscopic model, its map position is registered by the pencil point vertically beneath it.

11–14. Absolute Orientation. The projectors, having been oriented relative to each other, must be placed in their correct relation with respect to the map plot. This procedure, called the absolute orientation of the stereoscopic model, consists of adjusting it first to the map scale and second to the correct horizontal position.

11–15. Scale. The original projected model is at a random scale which may be determined by plotting two control points with the tracing stand. A comparison of this random scale with the desired scale gives a ratio of enlargement or reduction for moving the projectors, the original differences in X, Y, and Z readings being multiplied by this ratio to obtain corresponding new differences for setting the projectors to the required scale. It is advisable to check the new settings by again plotting the control points.

EXAMPLE 11–1. Scale readings for the projector settings at initial orientation are as follows:

	X	Y	Z
Projector I . . .	0 mm.	98.62 mm.	37.24 mm.
Projector II . . .	261.40 mm.	102.75 mm.	34.07 mm.
Differences . . .	261.40 mm.	4.13 mm.	3.17 mm.

The distance between control points, as plotted on the initial orientation, is found to be 292.60 mm. The corresponding ground distance is 10,276 ft., and the map scale is to be 1000 ft./in. Determine the new settings for the right-hand projector.

$$\text{Random scale} = \frac{10{,}276 \times 25.40}{292.60} = 892 \text{ ft./in.}$$

$$\text{Ratio (reduction)} = \frac{892}{1000} = 0.892$$

Multiplying this ratio by the differences above gives the following:

	X	Y	Z
New differences	233.17 mm.	3.68 mm.	2.83 mm.
Projector I	0 mm.	98.62 mm.	37.24 mm.
Projector II (new settings) . . .	233.17 mm.	102.30 mm.	34.41 mm.

11–16. Vertical Scale Readings. Since the stereoscopic model is a repro-duction of the actual ground surface, it is true to scale in all directions, so that its scale vertically is the same as its scale horizontally. The measuring scale on the tracing stand of course remains the same, regardless of the map scale. Therefore, a transformation ratio must be established to change scale readings to elevations or elevations to scale readings.

EXAMPLE 11–2. The tracing-stand scale reads 56.24 mm. when set on a point whose elevation is 580 ft. Map scale is 1000 ft./in. (a) Calculate the elevation of a point for which the scale reading is 62.08 mm. (b) Calculate the scale setting for the 500-ft. contour.

(a) Difference in scale readings = 62.08 − 56.24 = 5.84 mm.

$$\text{Difference in elevation} = \frac{5.84 \times 1000}{25.40} = 230 \text{ ft.}$$

Elevation of point = 580 + 230 = 810 ft.

(b) Difference in elevation = 580 − 500 = 80 ft.

$$\text{Difference in scale reading} = \frac{80 \times 25.40}{1000} = 2.03 \text{ mm.}$$

Scale reading for the 500-ft. contour = 56.24 − 2.03 = 54.21 mm.

11–17. Horizontalization. Three control points are used to horizontalize the model. The tracing stand is set at each point in turn, with the vertical scale giving the corresponding elevation, and the adjustment is made by tilting the two projectors as a unit until the three control points check both in position and elevation. Thus the model is brought both to the desired scale and into correct relation to the ground or map.

11–18. Plotting Details. For plotting a natural or cultural feature, the tracing stand is manipulated so that the floating mark appears to be at the point desired and the pencil is then depressed to mark its map location. In this way, point by point, the various details can be plotted. However, for items having continuity, such as roads and streams, the stand can be moved so that the floating mark appears to remain in continuous contact with the detail, while the disk is raised or lowered as may be needed according to the changes in elevation. The pencil point, left in its lowered position, traces out the detail on the map.

11–19. Contours. The plotting of a contour is similar to the plotting of a continuous planimetric feature, except that the vertical setting of the disk is kept constant at the elevation of the contour being plotted and locked to prevent any accidental movement. The stand is then moved over the model until the floating mark appears to be on the ground, thus locating a point on the contour. By moving the stand so that the floating mark keeps in apparent contact with the ground, the contour line is delineated on the map.

11–20. Bridging. The long carrier bar of the Multiplex allows several of the projectors to be set up at the same time (Fig. 11–16). With successive photographs inserted in these projectors, an entire strip can be oriented, starting with control at one end and continuing from one photograph to the next until control is reached at the other end. This process is called *bridging*

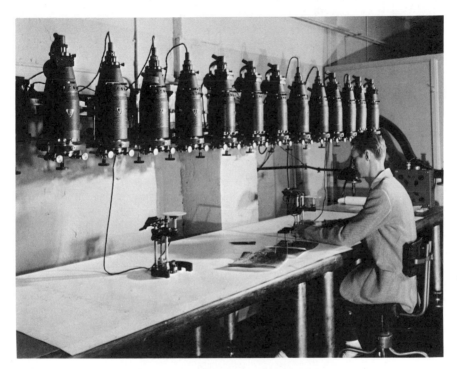

FIG. 11–16. Bridging between control with the long bar of the Multiplex Projector. (Courtesy of Air Survey Corporation.)

between control and eliminates the need for ground points on several intermediate photographs.

With Projectors I and II of a strip oriented as described previously, Projector III can be brought into orientation with II, then IV with III, and so on throughout the strip. It is to be noted that in the relative orientation after the first pair, all the movements must be made on one projector since the other is now already in correct position.*

If the first projection model were absolutely oriented, all the succeeding projectors should also be in correct absolute orientation, except for the

---

* Suggested procedure for relative orientation, all movements being on the right-hand projector: point 1, Y-movement; point 2, swing; point 3, Z-movement; point 4, X-tilt; point 5, Y-tilt, again overcorrecting. The point arrangement is the same as in Fig. 11–13.

accumulation of errors which will become apparent when the next line of control is reached. Any discrepancies are then distributed back through the flight strip. On the other hand, the first two projectors may be oriented only relatively, in which case the projectors of the entire strip will be in correct relative position with each other but not with respect to the map. Here the absolute orientation can be effected by control in the two end models only. It involves the determination of a ratio of enlargement or reduction for the entire strip which, applied to the differences in X, Y, and Z between successive projectors, determines new differences to give the required scale. Similarly, the entire flight can be horizontalized by adjusting the carrier bar until the elevations of projected control points at both ends agree with their true values.

11–21. *C* Factor. As an indication of the vertical plotting accuracy that may be expected from various instruments and as a guide in flight planning to meet specifications for contour interval, a quantity called the C factor is commonly used. This is defined as the ratio of the flying height to the least contour interval that can reasonably be expected to fulfill the usual accuracy requirements. Because of the many variables involved, this factor should be considered only as a guide rather than as an exact ratio. Some typical C factors for various instruments are as follows:

Stereotope	250
Multiplex	1000
Kelsh Plotter	1200
Wild A7	1500

12

OBLIQUE AND TERRESTRIAL PHOTOGRAPHS

12–1. Tri-Metrogon Photography. While vertical photography is the most widely used in surveying and mapping and presents the best introduction to a study of photogrammetry, there are mapping methods utilizing oblique photographs which are worthy of attention. One of these is the *tri-metrogon method*,* so called because it uses three photographs taken with wide-angled metrogon lenses at each exposure.

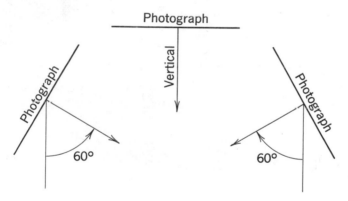

Fig. 12–1. Relative positions of tri-metrogon photographs.

The three photographs are located relatively, as shown in Fig. 12–1, the central one vertical and the others tilted perpendicular to the line of flight at depression angles of 30 degrees or at 60 degrees from the plumb line. The cameras are rigidly connected in this angular relationship (Fig. 12–2), and the shutters are made to act simultaneously. Since the lenses have an angular coverage of 74 degrees, it can be seen that each wing picture overlaps the vertical by 14 degrees and extends above the horizon by 7 degrees.

12–2. Flights. The photographs are taken in flights similar to those for ordinary vertical photography except that, because of the wide coverage made possible by the wing photographs, they can be spaced much wider

* Developed in 1941–42 jointly by the U. S. Geological Survey and the U. S. Army Air Corps.

apart, the distance being limited only by the ability to identify images in the small-scale background of the tilted photographs. A common spacing is about five or six times the distance for regular vertical photography. Thus there is a saving both in flying time and in the number of photographs. Providing quick coverage of large areas but with limitations as to accuracy, this method is especially useful for the rapid reconnaissance type of mapping.

The tri-metrogon photographs are used for mapping in much the same way as vertical photography, extending photographic control between lines

Fig. 12–2. Arrangement of tri-metrogon cameras in airplane. (Courtesy of Fairchild Camera & Instrument Corporation.)

of ground control by a radial-line network and transferring the planimetry by sketchmaster or similar instrument. The center photographs of the triads are of course used like any vertical photography. It is the differences in the use of the oblique lateral photographs that are discussed here.

12–3. Geometry. Figure 12-3 shows an oblique photograph of focal length f, tilted at angle t from the vertical. Lv is a vertical line, and o is the principal point of the photograph. Then $Lv = f \sec t$ and $ov = f \tan t$, the latter locating point v with respect to o; v may be recognized as the nadir point although, because of the extreme tilt, it does not actually fall on the photograph.

Horizontal directions are needed in making the radial-line templets, while directions as measured from the photograph are in its inclined plane.

Thus, for any point p, the photograph direction as measured from v is angle θ, while the corresponding horizontal angle is ϕ. Let x and y be the coordinates of p in the plane of the photograph, with v as origin and vo as the plus-y axis. It is evident that in the horizontal plane, x will remain the same, and the y-coordinate becomes $y \cos t$. Thus $\tan \theta = x/y$ and $\tan \phi = x/y \cos t$. With angle t known and the photograph coordinates x and y for any point measured, the corresponding horizontal angle ϕ can be calculated.

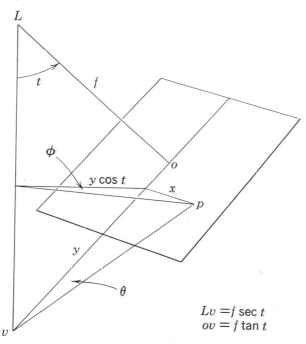

$$Lv = f \sec t$$
$$ov = f \tan t$$

Fig. 12–3. Relations in the oblique photograph.

12–4. Templets. To facilitate the construction of templets from the obliques, a special device called the Rectoblique Plotter* can be used. As shown in the schematic diagram in Fig. 12–4, the photograph is mounted under the left arm and the templet under the right arm. Then, with the proper setting, presently to be described, the angle between the principal line of the photograph and an etched line in the left radial arm represents the angle θ to any point, while the corresponding angle at the right arm is the angle ϕ, the two arms being connected by a bar shown at the top of the sketch.

Scales at v and R are for setting off the lengths that will provide the required relations. The radial point v is located at the calculated distance ov below the principal point and set by the scale at v. The distance a from

* Developed by J. G. Lewis in 1941.

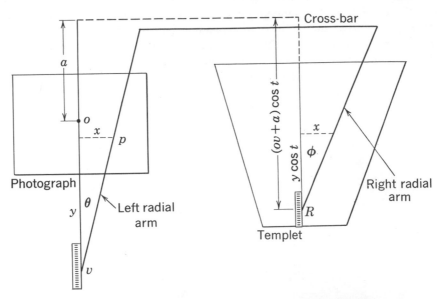

FIG. 12–4. Schematic diagram of the Rectoblique Plotter.

FIG. 12–5. Laying templets constructed from tri-metrogon photography. (Courtesy of Bausch & Lomb Optical Co.)

the principal point to the cross-bar is measured; then the right-hand pivot point R must be set at the distance $(ov + a) \cos t$ from the cross-bar.

As the left arm is placed on each of the desired points, the corresponding direction is fixed on the templet by the right arm. Since the photographs taken at a station are relatively known in their spatial relation, the three templets can be put together and used as a unit. These are then laid as in

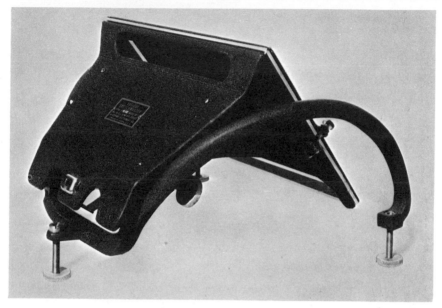

FIG. 12–6. Abrams oblique sketchmaster. (Photo from files of Gordon Enterprises.)

regular radial-line control, except that the arms of the wing templets will be much longer (Fig. 12–5).

12–5. Planimetry. The planimetry on the central vertical photographs can be traced to the map by means of one of the devices described in Chapter 6. For the obliques, a special device called the oblique sketchmaster is often used in which the photograph is held in its corresponding tilted plane, the map being horizontal. Points can then be matched and the intervening details traced out as in the vertical sketchmaster (Fig. 12–6).

12–6. Canadian Method. The Topographical Survey of Canada at one time used oblique photography in mapping large parts of the flat lake country of the Canadian Northwest Territories. Although not widely used in recent years, the method has long been considered something of a classical problem in photogrammetry and is developed briefly here for that reason rather than for any present practical importance. About the only similarity between it and the tri-metrogon method is that the photographs were also taken in groups of three. In the Canadian method, however, they were all high obliques, one pointing forward and one to each side at a horizontal angle of perhaps 45 degrees with the flight line. Furthermore, the three photographs at each "station" were taken in rapid succession with one camera rather than at the same instant with three interconnected cameras. Thus the three photographs were independent in so far as precise spatial relationships are concerned but could be used together in mapping because of their lateral overlap.

$$qw = Lq = f \sec\delta$$
$$Lv = f \operatorname{cosec}\delta$$
$$ov = f \cot\delta$$

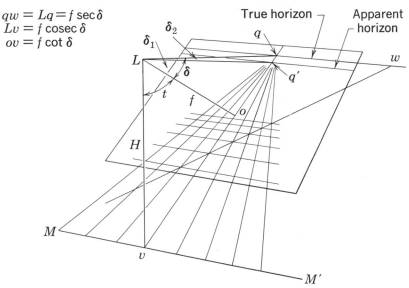

Fig. 12–7. Construction of a perspective grid.

12–7. Perspective Grid. This method was used in mapping terrain having little relief, so that the photograph scale depended only upon the vertical, the distance of the ground from the camera. The scale along any line perpendicular to the principal line was constant but different from that of any other line parallel to it, increasing in feet per inch (or other units) toward the background of the photograph. For each photograph it was thus possible to prepare a perspective grid upon which a trapezoidal section represented a square on the ground. If the grids were then oriented to the base map by means of ground control, a correspondence of grid areas to map areas could be established and the details delineated by careful inspection.

12–8. Grid Construction. In Fig. 12–7, L is the exposure station at altitude H above the ground, f is the camera focal length, and δ the angle of depression of the camera axis below the horizon, which, as photographed, appears near the top of the picture. The true horizon, however, is a small distance above this because of the altitude of the airplane above ground level. The principal point o, determined from the fiducial marks on the photograph, and the apparent horizon, located directly upon the photograph by inspection, provide references for subsequent measurement and construction.

The dip of the apparent horizon δ_2, due to the flying height H and allowing for the effect of atmospheric refraction, is $58.8 \sqrt{H}$ seconds. The value of oq' can be measured directly from the photograph; then $\tan \delta_1 = oq'/f$, $\delta = \delta_1 + \delta_2$, and $oq = f \tan \delta$, which thus locates the true horizon. Also $ov = f \cot \delta$.

The base map was divided into 1-inch squares plotted to the scale 1 in. = 660 ft. Therefore, lines on any portion of the photograph grid must be spaced a distance that represents 660 ft. The scale of the line MM' perpendicular to the principal line through v is $S_v = H/f \csc \delta$ ft./in., so the required grid spacing along this line is $660/S_v$ inches. Each of these division points is then connected by a straight line with q, the vanishing point for all lines parallel to the principal line, thus locating the grid lines in one direction. In the other direction the lines will be parallel, their vanishing points being at infinity, so all that is needed is to determine their spacing along the principal line. For this, a diagonal of the system is drawn, which of course will form a diagonal of the squares between each pair of adjoining lines already drawn. The vanishing points for all diagonals, being at 45 degrees (horizontally) with the principal line, will be on the true horizon at a distance from q equal to Lq or $f \sec \delta$. One of these points has been plotted at w. Any line now drawn through w to intersect the longitudinal lines already drawn will represent the diagonals of a series of the 660-ft. squares. The grid is completed by drawing lines perpendicular to the principal line at the intersection of this diagonal with each longitudinal line.

12–9. Convergent Photography. A method of photogrammetric mapping using so-called convergent low oblique photographs was developed by the U. S. Geological Survey around 1950. The term *low oblique*, it will be remembered, applies to a photograph which is deliberately tilted at a considerable angle from the vertical but not enough to show the horizon. It does not refer to the flying altitude, which as a matter of fact may be greater than that for vertical photography of corresponding accuracy. In this method, two photographs are taken simultaneously at a station, each with the camera axis at an angle of 20 degrees from the vertical, the two cameras being connected so that the angular relations are rigidly maintained (Fig. 12–8.)

The photographs may be taken either with the cameras pointed forward and backward along the flight line or laterally at right angles to it. In the first way, the forward photograph at one station overlaps the backward photograph at the following station; while in the second way, the two photographs at each station overlap those in either direction much the same

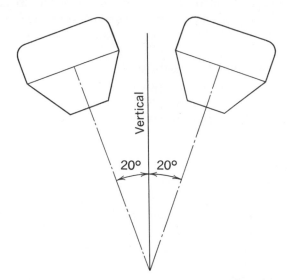

FIG. 12–8. Position of cameras for convergent photography.

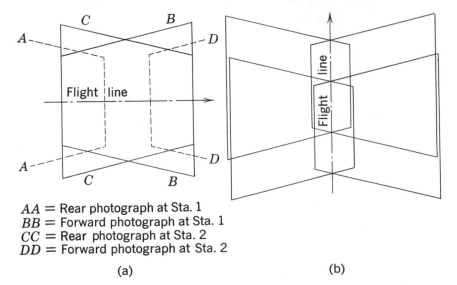

AA = Rear photograph at Sta. 1
BB = Forward photograph at Sta. 1
CC = Rear photograph at Sta. 2
DD = Forward photograph at Sta. 2

(a)   (b)

FIG. 12–9. Diagram showing overlap of low oblique photographs: (a) convergent coverage, (b) transverse coverage.

as in vertical photography but covering a considerably wider strip. These different overlaps are shown in Fig. 12–9.

12–10. Projection Instruments. The photographs are used for mapping or control plotting in a projection instrument wherein the projectors are placed in the same relative positions as the cameras themselves. These instruments are similar to the ordinary Multiplex described in Chapter 11, modified to allow for the larger amounts of tilt. The Twinplex Plotter, devised by the U. S. Geological Survey, and the Balplex Plotter (Fig. 11–8) are examples of the equipment adaptable to this type of photography. Except for the fact that the pictures are obliques, the principles are the same as for the projection of vertical photography. Corresponding rays to the same points from two pictures intersect in space in the projected model. Since the photographs are projected dichromatically, they can be viewed stereoscopically with the proper spectacles, and the floating mark of the tracing stand can be set at the ground surface for plotting.

12–11. Advantages. The overlap in convergent photographs may be as much as 100 per cent, which increases the ratio of exposure station base to flying height over that of ordinary vertical photography. This considerably increases the vertical accuracy at the expense of some decrease in the horizontal. However, the latter is not usually serious, while an increased vertical accuracy is greatly to be desired. Putting it another way, to obtain the same vertical accuracy as that provided by the corresponding vertical photographs, a higher flying height can be used; this in turn increases the coverage of each model over an already increased amount resulting from the greater overlap. Perhaps the most important advantage of all is the increased stereoscopic perception obtainable with the increased base-height ratio, which affords a more precise setting of the tracing stand at the ground surface.

12–12. Disadvantages. A major disadvantage, aside from the somewhat lessened horizontal accuracy, is the increased possibility of hidden areas resulting from topographic relief or high structures. This is a result of the larger vertical angles at the outer reaches of the photograph, as indicated in Fig. 12–10. However, unless the elevation differences are great, this is not likely to be serious and of course occurs to some extent even in vertical photography. The advantages of convergent photography for production mapping purposes appear to outweigh the disadvantages, except in unusual circumstances.

Terrestrial Photogrammetry

12–13. Comparison with Aerial Photographs. Photographs taken at ground stations were used in surveying and mapping for several years prior to the development of aerial photography but have now been largely supplanted by the latter. This is understandable when it is considered how much more area can be covered, together with the relative freedom from obstructions. However, the terrestrial photograph does offer some advantages. Its camera station is at a fixed point, which can be marked and readily located with respect to the control, whereas that of the aerial photograph can be determined only indirectly by space resection methods. Furthermore, the ground camera can be set up, leveled, and pointed in a given direction which can be measured. The aerial camera, on the other hand, cannot be accurately leveled because of acceleration displacements of the bubbles, thus introducing tilt which, like the camera station itself, can be determined only by some indirect method.

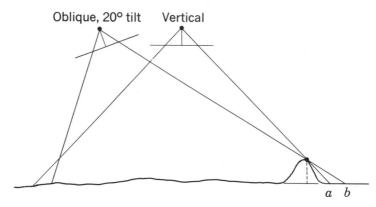

FIG. 12–10. Extent of hidden ground resulting from relief *a* in a vertical photograph, *b* in an oblique photograph, both having the same angular coverage.

12–14. Present Use. Terrestrial photogrammetry is now largely used as a supplementary aid where some features of the terrain do not fully show on the aerial views, as gorges or river channels having very steep and possibly overhanging banks. Camera stations may be set on one side and photographs taken of the opposite bank. Plotting from this type of photography can then be tied in with the main part of the work obtained through the aerial survey. Of course, there may be instances where the terrestrial plot constitutes the entire project. Some of the field equipment used in terrestrial photographic surveying is illustrated in Fig. 12–11.

12–15. Camera. The terrestrial surveying camera is mounted on a tripod and is furnished both with a plumbing device for setting exactly over a ground station and with levels for making the camera axis horizontal. It may also be provided with telescope and circles so that the direction of the camera axis can be determined (Fig. 12–12). In another type, the theodolite head is interchangeable with the camera without disturbing the setting of the tripod.

12–16. Camera Stations. The photographs are taken to provide overlapping areas of adjacent pictures similar to those of aerial photography. However, the camera stations must be carefully selected to avoid the obstruction of details by terrain or objects in the foreground. In order to provide sufficient coverage, two or three photographs may be taken at each station with the camera axis pointing in different directions, as shown in Fig. 12–13. Thus the terrestrial camera stations may not form as regular a pattern as those for aerial photography. On the other hand, control may be somewhat simpler, since the camera stations themselves can be located directly by survey, which, of course, is impossible for aerial photographs.

FIG. 12–11. Field equipment for terrestrial photographic surveying, including phototheodolite, subtense bar, and targets. (Courtesy of Wild Heerbrugg Instruments, Inc.)

12–17. Single Photographs. Although photographs are not often used singly to determine the locations of points, it is possible to do so, provided the elevations of the latter are known by some other means. Figure 12–14(a) represents a terrestrial photograph, the ground station and orientation of which are known. The plan view (b) shows the photograph trace on the

Fig. 12–12. Zeiss phototheodolite for terrestrial photogrammetry. (Courtesy of Transmares Corporation.)

horizontal plane through the camera axis with the focal length f plotted from the principal point. L is the known station of the camera, and Lo is plotted in the known direction of the camera axis. It is desired to locate the map position of a point P, whose coordinates are x_p and y_p on the photograph and whose elevation is h_p above the camera station.

12–18. Construction. For a graphical solution, the value of $x_p(= ok)$ is laid off on the photograph trace and a line of indefinite extent drawn through k from L. The map location of P is somewhere on this line. The value of y_p $(= kq)$ is then laid off perpendicular to Lk, this construction representing the vertical plane containing the camera station and point P, which will be

FIG. 12–13. Directions of the camera axis at terrestrial stations.

somewhere on a line of indefinite extent drawn through L and q. At any convenient point on Lk, produced and perpendicular to it, the value of h_p is laid off to the scale of the ground survey. Through the end of this perpendicular a line is drawn parallel to Lk to an intersection with Lq produced. A line from this point perpendicular to Lk then locates the map position of P. It will be noted that the strength of this determination increases with the difference in elevation h and becomes indeterminate for points at or near the same level as the camera.

12–19. Computation. The location of P can also be determined by computation:

$$\tan \alpha = \frac{x_p}{f} \qquad (12\text{–}1)$$

$$\tan m = \frac{y_p}{f \sec \alpha} \qquad (12\text{–}2)$$

$$LP = \frac{h}{\tan m} \qquad (12\text{–}3)$$

12–20. Direction of Camera Axis. The direction of the camera axis, if unknown, can be found, provided one control point appears in the picture as at A in Fig. 12–14(c). A point a_1 is plotted on LA at a distance from L equal to $\sqrt{f^2 + x_a^2}$, an arc of radius f is swung with L as center, and an arc of radius x_a is swung with a_1 as center. The intersection of these arcs locates the principal point o, and the photograph trace is defined by the line through o

and a_1. The direction of Lo can also be found by calculation, since $\tan \alpha_a = x_a/f$.

EXAMPLE 12–1. A terrestrial photograph taken at a station L contains images of a control point A and a new point P. Survey and photograph coordinates are as follows:

	Ground			Photograph	
	X (ft.)	Y (ft.)	Z (ft.)	x (in.)	y (in.)
L	3200	4750	850	–	–
A	1630	5820	–	–2.468	–
P	–	–	1240	+2.890	+1.764

Determine the coordinates of P. Focal length of the camera is 10 in.

$$\tan \text{Az}_{LA} = \frac{1570}{1070} = 1.4673 \qquad \text{Az}_{LA} = 304°\ 16'$$

$$\tan \alpha_A = \frac{2.468}{10} = 0.2468 \qquad \alpha_A = \underline{+13°\ 52'}$$

$$\text{Az}_{LO} = 318°\ 08'$$

$$\tan \alpha_P = \frac{2.890}{10} = 0.2890 \qquad \alpha_P = \underline{+16°\ 07'}$$

$$\text{Az}_{LP} = 334°\ 15'$$

$$\tan m_P = \frac{1.764}{10 \times 1.0409} = 0.1695$$

$$LP = \frac{h}{\tan m} = \frac{390}{0.1695} = 2301 \text{ ft.}$$

$$\Delta X = LP \sin \text{Az}_{LP} \qquad\qquad \Delta Y = LP \cos \text{Az}_{LP}$$
$$= 2301 \times 0.4345 \qquad\qquad\quad = 2301 \times 0.9007$$
$$= -1000 \qquad\qquad\qquad\quad = +2073$$
$$X_P = 2200 \text{ ft.} \qquad\qquad\qquad Y_P = 6823 \text{ ft.}$$

The accuracy of this location of P will depend both upon the value of h and the accuracy with which h is determined. In this example, an error of 5 ft. in the elevation of P will introduce an error of almost 30 ft. in its position.

12–21. Two Photographs. A general situation will be considered in which the photographs are taken at camera stations of known position, the directions of the camera axes have not been previously determined, neither camera station appears on the other photograph, and there is at least one control point appearing in each picture. It is desired to determine the orientation of each photograph and the ground coordinates (X, Y, and Z) of new points within the area of overlap. Most other cases are variations of this basic problem.

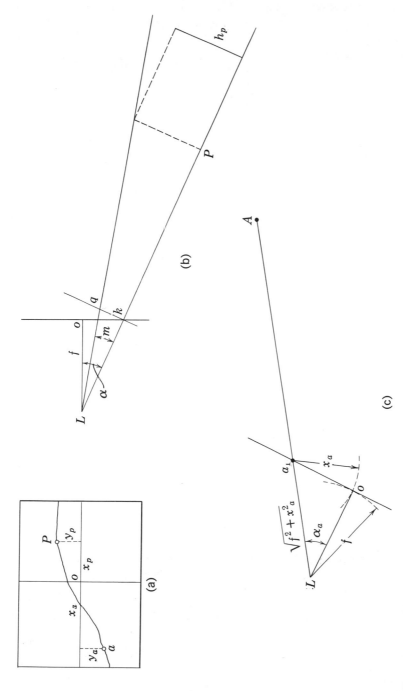

Fig. 12–14. (a) A terrestrial photograph. (b) Construction to locate P when h_p is known. Lok is horizontal, while Lkq is vertical. (c) Construction to determine the direction of Lo.

12–22. Orientation. In Fig. 12–15, A represents a ground control point which is photographed at a_1 and a_2 on photographs 1 and 2, respectively. The coordinates x_{a_1} and y_{a_1} are measured with respect to the axes of the left photograph. Then x_{a_1} will appear in the plan view, as shown. The azimuth of L_1A can be determined from the survey coordinates and α will be $\tan^{-1}(x_{a_1}/f)$, which when applied to the azimuth of L_1A gives the azimuth

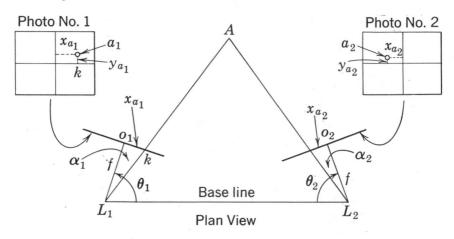

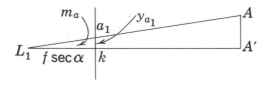

Vertical Section

FIG. 12–15. Surveying with two photographs.

of the photograph axis Lo_1. The azimuth of Lo_2 can be determined by a similar computation.

12–23. Elevations. The elevations of L_1 and A are related as shown in the vertical section of Fig. 12–15. The ground distance obtained from the survey is the horizontal projection L_1A'. Then the vertical angle m_a is $\tan^{-1}\dfrac{y_{a_1}}{f\sec\alpha}$ and the difference in elevation AA' is $L_1A'\tan m_a$, from which the elevation of L_1 can be found. In like manner, the elevation of L_2 can be determined.

12–24. New Points. The calculations for a new point are essentially the reverse of the above process. If A now represents the new point, angles α_1

and α_2 are calculated from coordinates measured on the pictures and, when applied to the azimuths of $L_1 o_1$ and $L_2 o_2$, give the ground azimuths of the lines $L_1 A$ and $L_2 A$. The coordinates of A are then determined by finding the intersection of these lines. The difference in elevation from L_1 and A is found by means of the computed vertical angle and from this the elevation of A is determined. A check is obtained by a similar computation from L_2.

EXAMPLE 12–2. Terrestrial photographs taken from two stations, L_1 and L_2, contain images of a control point A and a new point P. Survey and photograph coordinates are as follows:

	X (ft.)	Y (ft.)	Z (ft.)	Left Photo, L_1		Right Photo, L_2	
				x (in.)	y (in.)	x (in.)	y (in.)
L_1	0	0	560				
L_2	2000	0	680				
A	710	1776	435	-1.802	-0.664	-2.878	-1.163
P				$+2.751$	$+1.164$	$+1.159$	$+0.844$

Determine the coordinates of P. Focal length of the camera is 10 in.

Left Photo

$$\tan \mathrm{Az}_{L_1 A} = \frac{710}{1776} = 0.39977 \qquad \mathrm{Az}_{L_1 A} = 21° \, 48'$$

$$\tan o L_1 a = \frac{-1.802}{10} = 0.1802 \qquad o L_1 a = \underline{10° \, 13'}$$

$$\text{Azimuth of camera axis} = 32° \, 01'$$

$$\tan o L_1 p = \frac{2.751}{10} = 0.2751 \qquad o L_1 p = \underline{15° \, 23'}$$

$$\mathrm{Az}_{L_1 P} = 47° \, 24'$$

Right Photo

$$\tan \mathrm{Az}_{L_2 A} = \frac{-1290}{1776} = 0.72635 \qquad \mathrm{Az}_{L_2 A} = 324° \, 00'$$

$$\tan o L_2 a = \frac{-2.878}{10} = 0.2878 \qquad o L_2 a = \underline{16° \, 03'}$$

$$\text{Azimuth of camera axis} = 340° \, 03'$$

$$\tan o L_2 p = \frac{1.159}{10} = 0.1159 \qquad o L_2 p = \underline{6° \, 37'}$$

$$\mathrm{Az}_{L_2 P} = 346° \, 40'$$

$$\frac{x_P - 0}{y_P - 0} = \tan 47° \, 24' = 1.0875 \qquad x_P = 1.0875 \, y_P$$

$$\frac{x_P - 2000}{y_P - 0} = \tan 346° \, 40' = -0.23700 \quad \underline{x_P = -0.2370 \, y_P + 2000}$$

$$1.0875 \, y_P = -0.2370 \, y_P + 2000$$

$$+ \, 1.3245 \, y_P = +2000$$

Coordinates of P $\qquad \begin{cases} y_P = +1510 \text{ ft.} \\ x_P = 1.0875 \times 1510 = +1642 \text{ ft.} \end{cases}$

$$L_1P = \sqrt{(1642)^2 + (1510)^2} = 2231$$

$$L_2P = \sqrt{(358)^2 + (1510)^2} = 1552$$

Left Photo   *Right Photo*

f sec 15° 23′ = 10 × 1.03716 = 10.372 f sec 6° 37′ = 10 × 1.00671 = 10.067

$$\tan m_P = \frac{+1.164}{10.372} = +0.11223 \qquad\qquad \tan m_P = \frac{+0.844}{10.067} = +0.08384$$

Diff. elev. = $L_1P \tan m_P$ Diff. elev. = $L_2P \tan m_P$

= 2231 × 0.11223   = 1552 × 0.08384

= +250 ft.   = +130 ft.

Elevation L_1 =   560   Elevation L_2 =   680

Elevation P =   810 ft.   Elevation P =   810 ft.

12–25. Plotting Instruments. Some of the automatic plotting instruments mentioned in Chapter 11, as for example the Zeiss Stereoplanigraph, are adaptable for mapping with terrestrial as well as aerial photographs. If the pictures are considered as aerial views rotated 90 degrees about the base line connecting the camera stations, it will be seen that parallax difference is a measure of the horizontal distance from this base. If the latter is taken as the x-axis, then the parallax will vary with the y-coordinate. Thus, the handwheels serve to move the floating mark in the X- and Z-directions while the foot control governs the Y-movement.

PROBLEMS

12–1. The survey coordinates for the exposure station of a terrestrial photograph are: $X = 8465$ ft., $Y = 12,120$ ft., $Z = 875$ ft. Camera focal length is 6.00 in. and the azimuth of the camera axis is 157° 20′. Calculate the survey coordinates of the following points:

Point	Photograph Coordinates		Elevation (ft.)
	x (in.)	y (in.)	
a	+3.070	+1.562	962
b	−2.682	+0.874	937
c	−3.457	−1.072	790
d	+2.904	−2.384	654

12–2. The horizontal coordinates for the exposure station of a terrestrial photograph are: $X = 18,340$ ft., $Y = 14,265$ ft. The survey coordinates of a control point are: $X = 19,560$ ft., $Y = 16,685$ ft., $Z = 1550$ ft. Camera focal length is 8.25 in., and the photograph coordinates of the control point are: $x = +2.475$ in., $y = +0.372$ in. Calculate the azimuth of the camera axis and the elevation of the camera.

12–3. The coordinates of a second point on the photograph of Prob. 12–2 are: $x = -2.346$ in., $y = +1.208$ in. Determine its survey coordinates if its elevation is 1720 ft.

12–4. The coordinates of a third point on the photograph of Prob. 10–2 are: $x = +3.846$ in., $y = -0.246$ in. The point is known to be 4850 ft. from the camera station. Calculate the point's elevation.

12–5. Two terrestrial photographs are taken such that each camera station appears on the other picture, the image coordinates being as follows:

Image of L_2 on L_1: $x = +3.805$ in., $y = +0.763$ in.

Image of L_1 on L_2: $x = -2.982$ in., $y = $ Not given

The distance L_1L_2 is 2140 ft., L_2 is due east of L_1, the elevation of L_1 is 630 ft., and the focal length is 12 in. Calculate the direction of the camera axis at each station. Also determine the theoretical value of the y-coordinate not given above.

12–6. The following coordinates are measured for a point which appears on the photographs of Prob. 12–5:

On Photo at L_1		On Photo at L_2	
x (in.)	y (in.)	x (in.)	y (in.)
−0.482	+1.372	+1.038	Not given

Calculate the position of this point with respect to L_1L_2, its elevation, and the theoretical value of the coordinate not given.

12–7. Two terrestrial photographs are taken 3000 ft. apart with the camera axis perpendicular to the line between the stations. The focal length is 8.25 in. and the elevation of the left camera is 1284 ft. Following are the coordinates of a point which appears on both pictures:

On Left Photo		On Right Photo	
x (in.)	y (in.)	x (in.)	y (in.)
+3.209	−0.762	−3.887	+0.146

Calculate the elevation and position (with respect to the base line) of the point and the elevation of the camera at the right station.

12–8. The survey coordinates of two terrestrial photograph stations and a control point are as follows:

Point	X (ft.)	Y (ft.)	Z (ft.)
L_1	6,280	9,462	–
L_2	9,305	8,975	–
A	10,085	11,282	915

The following photograph coordinates were measured:

Point	On Photo at L_1		On Photo at L_2	
	x (in.)	y (in.)	x (in.)	y (in.)
a	$+1.724$	-0.336	-0.204	$+0.425$

Focal length of the camera is 6.00 in. Calculate the azimuth of the camera axis and the elevation of the camera at each station.

12–9. The following coordinates for a new point are measured on the photographs of Prob. 12–8.

On photo at L_1: $x = -2.904$ in., $y = +1.136$ in.

On photo at L_2: $x = -0.873$ in.

Calculate the survey coordinates and elevation of the new point and the theoretical value for the y-coordinate on the photograph at L_2.

13

APPLICATIONS

13-1. General. The uses of aerial photographs are not only numerous but are rapidly expanding into fields other than engineering. There is room here to consider only a few of the more outstanding examples of common applications.

13-2. Map and Photograph Scales. Undoubtedly one of the most important uses of photogrammetry is in the preparation of maps, both planimetric and topographic. These are made for many different purposes, for each of which a certain range of scale may be preferred. According to one photogrammetric firm,* scales for maps and aerial photography have been divided into three groups as follows:

Group I, from 1:600 to 1:2500.
Group II, from 1:2500 to 1:125,000.
Group III, from 1:125,000 to 1:1,000,000.

Scale groups recommended by this firm for some typical uses are shown in the following listing:

Aeronautical charts, II and III
Airport planning and design, I
City maps and planning, I
County maps and planning, I and II
Drainage studies, I, II, and III
Flood control, II and III
Forestry and lumbering, II
Geology, I, II, and III
Highway planning and construction, I and II
Industrial planning and area development, I
Irrigation, II and III
Land classification, II and III

Levees, I and II
Mosaics, I
Power and telephone lines, I and II
Quadrangle mapping, II and III
Railroad construction, I and II
Real estate development, I
River and harbor development, I
Sewer and water systems, I
Soil conservation, I and II
Stockpile inventories, I
Strip mining, I
Tax maps, I and II
Traffic studies, I
Zoning, I and II

Besides the information it gives regarding recommended scales, this list effectively presents the varied purposes to which photogrammetric operations can be put.

* Michael Baker, Jr., Air Maps, Inc.

13-3. Topographic Mapping. An outstanding example of topographic mapping is the production of the quadrangle sheets issued by the U. S. Geological Survey, which now does most of the subsidiary control and practically all of the detail plotting, including contours, by photogrammetric

FIG. 13-1. Proposed railroad location plotted on aerial photograph. (Courtesy of Chicago, Burlington & Quincy Railroad Company.)

methods. There is probably more photogrammetric equipment used in the Survey's four regional offices than in any similar mapping organization. This may well be realized when it is considered that the U. S. Geological Survey is charged with the topographic mapping of the entire country, a job which is far from completed at modern standards.

Other agencies responsible for mapping areas of great extent find aerial photographic methods almost indispensable; the U. S. Coast and Geodetic Survey in the preparation of the coastal and aeronautical charts; the U. S. Forest Service in making land acquisition and administrative maps; and the military services for their mapping needs. These are but a very few of the mapping agencies which utilize aerial photography; a complete list would include many more national and state services, as well as numerous private organizations.

13–4. Route Planning. Probably no modern major highway project is now planned without the aid of an aerial survey, the extent of its use varying with the length of the project and the terrain through which it passes. Photogrammetry is invaluable in reconnaissance, whereby the various possible routes can be discerned more rapidly and with more certainty than by any ground method and without entering private lands. More than this, in some instances, practically the entire paper location has been accomplished by photogrammetric means, and even earthwork volumes on a few jobs have been determined to the satisfaction of both the contractor and the contracting agency.

The use of aerial photographs in railroad location is shown in Fig. 13–1. On this project, the photographs were used as planimetric maps, which greatly reduced the field measurements and drafting work ordinarily required by conventional ground methods.

Aerial surveys are equally valuable in the planning of routes for waterways, pipe lines, and electric transmission lines. An example of the last is shown in Fig. 13–2.

13–5. Geology. Aerial photographs are used in geological and mining exploratory work, in which they are viewed and interpreted directly in addition to being used in the preparation of maps. Inventories of surface stockpile in connection with mining operations can also be made by photogrammetric measurements.

With reference to Fig. 13–3, which shows a photograph of a dense jungle area,

the indicated surface geology could not have been mapped readily by any other means. At the top and left is a system of dipping beds. Starting at the top center is an apparent fault zone, along which there appears to be a different type of vegetation and an apparent displacement of the beds. Directly below and slightly to the right of the apparent termination of this fault zone is an area which suggests a remnant of an old alluvial fan, as evidenced by a difference in vegetation and the erosional pattern. In a four-o'clock direction from the upper point of the fan, and extending along its upper right edge, is an apparent fault. Note the stream offset in the lower center, which may be a continuation of the first-mentioned fault. About an inch to the right of this major offset is a small offset which might also indicate some displacement due to movement along a possible secondary fault, which extends in a twelve o'clock direction.*

* Fairchild Aerial Surveys, Inc., *Focusing on Facts*, p. 11.

FIG. 13–2. Pair of photographs showing proposed relocation of transmission line. Placing the new line as marked by the circles would shorten the existing line 9.4 per cent and would use four fewer towers. These photographs are oriented for viewing with a small pocket-type stereoscope. (Courtesy of Fairchild Aerial Surveys, Inc.)

13-6. Forestry. Maps prepared from aerial photographs are used in forestry and lumbering operations to plan and develop roads, trails, buildings, telephone lines, and camp sites, and as aids in fire prevention and control.

Fɪɢ. 13-3. Photograph of a dense jungle area. (Courtesy of Fairchild Aerial Surveys, Inc.)

Furthermore, the aerial survey is useful in cruising and for the volume estimation and evaluation of timber. The photographs themselves may be used to determine the areas of forest coverage, something of the nature of the trees, their height, the per cent of coverage, crown diameters, and to inventory storage piles.

13–7. Tax Maps. A use of aerial photography which has proved worth more than its cost is the preparation of tax maps in many communities. The profit has resulted from more accurate delineation of property, often with increased assessments as a consequence, and, what is perhaps more remarkable, the actual discovery of many pieces of land previously missed on the tax rolls.

13–8. Farm Areas. The Agricultural Stabilization and Conservation Service uses aerial photographs for measuring areas of farm crops to check compliance with the various control programs. Upon identification of the fields, their areas are determined on the photograph with a planimeter and then changed to ground areas by means of the photographic scales previously determined.

While these are but a few of the ways in which aerial photography is being used other than in a purely pictorial sense, they should nevertheless suggest the widespread applications of this field.

INDEX